Harmless Snakes
of the West

Brian Hubbs

First Edition

Tricolor Books

Manufactured in the United States of America
Library of Congress Control Number: 2013936762
ISBN 13: 978-0-9754641-4-4
All photos by Brian Hubbs unless otherwise noted.
Cover design by Brian Hubbs and Gary Thomas.
Layout and design by Brian Hubbs and Zu Raad.
All trademarks used herein are for identification
purposes only and are used without
intent to infringe on the owner's trademarks
or other proprietary rights.

Cover Photos (Clockwise from upper left): Painted Desert Glossy Snake (*Arizona elegans philipi*) by Brian Hubbs, Rough Green Snake (*Opheodrys aestivus*) by Phil Peak, California Kingsnake (*Lampropeltis getula californiae*) by Brian Hubbs, Eastern Hog-nosed Snake (*Heterodon platirhinos*) by Matt Cage, Eastern Yellow-bellied Racer (*Coluber constrictor flaviventris*) by Matt Cage, Organ Pipe Shovel-nosed Snake (*Chionactis palarostris organica*) by Brian Hubbs, Coastal Rosy Boa (*Lichanura trivirgata roseofusca*) by Brian Hubbs, and Gray-banded Kingsnake (*Lampropeltis alterna*) by Brian Hubbs.

Back Cover: San Francisco Garter Snake (*Thamnophis sirtalis tetrataenia*) by Brian Hubbs.

Second Printing - November, 2014

Natural Histories and Guides from Tricolor Books

Mountain Kings
Brian Hubbs
© 2004 – 312 pages – In Print – ISBN: 0-9754641-0-8
ISBN 13: 978-0-9754641-0-6
$45.00

Common Kingsnakes
The Natural History of Lampropeltis getula
Brian Hubbs
© 2009 – 436 pages – In Print –ISBN 13: 978-0-9754641-1-3
$60.00

A Guide to the Rattlesnakes
and other Venomous Serpents of the United States
Brian Hubbs and Brendan O'Connor
© 2012 – 132 pages – In Print – ISBN 13: 978-0-9754641-3-7
$19.95

Harmless Snakes
of the West
Brian Hubbs
© 2013 – 130 pages – In Print – ISBN 13: 978-0-9754641-4-4
$19.95

To order any of these publications, please write the publisher:
E-mail: tricolorbrian@hotmail.com
Phone: 480-456-5202

About the Author

Brian Hubbs lives, works, writes, and plays in Arizona. However, he searches for reptiles and amphibians (herps) all over the United States. He is an amateur field herpetologist who has been expanding his interests for over 40 years. He is an authority on kingsnakes (Lampropeltis), has already authored two large natural histories for those serpents, Common Kingsnakes and Mountain Kings, and has a third kingsnake book nearly completed. He is addicted to exploring the natural world, and an advocate of "common sense" conservation and "wise-use" policies toward wildlife and habitat.

Contents

Acknowledgements 5
Introduction 6
What Are Snakes? 9

Species and Subspecies Accounts

Blind Snakes *(Rena dissectus, humilis, & dulcis)* 12
Rubber Boa *(Charina bottae)* 14
Rosy Boa *(Lichanura trivirgata)* 16
Glossy Snake *(Arizona elegans)* 20
Worm Snake *(Carphophis vermis)* 22
Scarletsnake *(Cemophora coccinea)* 23
Variable Sandsnake *(Chilomeniscus stramineus)* 25
Shovel-nosed Snakes *(Chionactis occipitalis, & palarostris)* 26
Racers *(Coluber constrictor & Drymobius margaritiferus)* 29
Regal Black-striped Snake *(Coniophanes imperialis)* 32
Sharp-tailed Snakes *(Contia longicaudae, & tenuis)* 33
Ring-necked Snake *(Diadophis punctatus)* 35
Texas Indigo Snake *(Drymarchon melanurus)* 38
Western Mud Snake *(Farancia abacura)* 40
Hook-nosed Snakes *(Ficimia streckeri, Gyalopian canum, & G. quadrangulare)* 42
Hog-nosed Snakes *(Heterodon)*
  (H. gloydi, H. kennerlyi, H. nasicus, & H. platirhinos) 44
Night Snakes *(Hypsiglena chlorophaea, jani, & ochrorhyncha)* 47
Gray-banded Kingsnake *(Lampropeltis alterna)* 49
Prairie Kingsnake *(Lampropeltis calligaster)* 51
Common Kingsnake *(Lampropeltis getula)* 53
Mountain Kingsnakes *(Lampropeltis pyromelana & zonata)* 58
Milk Snake *(Lampropeltis triangulum)* 62
Cat-eyed Snake *(Leptodeira septentrionalis)* 66
Whipsnakes *(Masticophis)*
  (M. flagellum, M. lateralis, M. taeniatus, M. schotti, & M. bilineatus) 67
Water Snakes & Salt Marsh Snakes *(Nerodia)*
  (N. clarkia, N. erythrogaster, N. fasciata, N. harteri,
    N. rhombifer, & N. sipedon) 74
Green Snakes *(Ophyodrys vernalis & aestivus)* 78
Brown Vine Snake *(Oxybelis aeneus)* 80
Rat Snakes & Fox Snake *(Pantherophis, Bogertophis, & Senticolis)*
  (Pantherophis bairdi, P.emoryi, P. obsoletus, P. vulpinus,
    Bogertophis subocularis, & Senticolis triaspis) 81
Leaf-nosed Snakes *(Phyllorhynchus decurtatus & browni)* 86
Bull, Gopher, & Pine Snakes *(Pituophis catenifer & ruthveni)* 88
Crayfish Snakes *(Regina grahamii & rigida)* 92
Long-nosed Snake *(Rhinocheilus lecontei)* 94
Patch-nosed Snakes *(Salvadora grahamiae & hexalepis)* 96
Ground Snake *(Sonora semiannulata)* 99
Brown & Red-bellied Snakes *(Storeria dekayi & occipitomaculata)* 101
Black-headed Snakes & Flat-headed Snakes *(Tantilla)*
  (T. atriceps, T. cucullata, T. hobartsmithi, T. nigriceps,
    T. planiceps, T. wilcoxi, T. yaquia, & T. gracilis) 104

Contents (Con't)

Aquatic Garter Snakes (*Thamnophis*)
(*T. atratus, T. couchi, T. eques, T. gigas, T. hammondii,*
T. proximus, & T. rufipuntatus) 107
Terrestrial Garter Snakes (*Thamnophis*)
(*T. cyrtopsis, T. elegans, T. marcianus, T. ordinoides, & T. radix*) 113
Common Garter Snakes (*Thamnophis sirtalis*)..118
Lyre Snakes (*Trimorphodon lambda, lyrophanes, & vilkinsonii*) 123
Lined snake (*Tropidoclonion lineatum*) 125
Earth Snakes (*Virginia valeria & striatula*) 127
Reference Bibliography...129
Notes..130

Acknowledgements

While much of what is written here was researched from the works of other authors, a great deal was contributed from my experiences and those of other field herpetologists. I would like to thank the following people for sharing interesting information and insights, critiquing maps and chapters, guiding me to find snakes to photograph, or just passing on words of encouragement: Carlo Bongio, Jeff Boundy, Brandon DeCavele, Dave Doherty, Matt Dunaetz, Jeremiah Easter, Robert Edwards, Roy Engeldorf, Will Flaxington, Dan Fogell, John Fraser, Troy Hibbitts, Brian Hinds, Richard Hoyer, David Jahn, Dan Johnson, Danny Lawrence, Bobby MacGregor, Brian M. McGurty, Mitchell Mulks, Sam Murray, Gus Rentfro, Alan St. John, Curtis Schmidt, J.P. Stephenson, Travis Taggart, David Tobler, Scott Wahlberg, Mike Waters, and Chad Whitney.

I would also like to express my appreciation to the people who generously contributed many needed photographs: Matt Cage, Robert Edwards, Joseph Forks, Troy Hibbitts, Brian Hinds, David Jahn, Ben Jones, Bill Love, Sam Murray, Gary Nafis, Phil Peak, Richard Porter, Clint Pustejovsky, Alan St. John, Jordan Shume, J.P. Stephenson, and David Tobler.

Introduction

Many have heard of snakes, but few know much about them. For instance, there are many types of snake in the western U.S. They come in small, medium, and large sizes, and bright to dull colors. Temperatures differ from species to species, as well as their favored prey. Some are desert dwellers, while others prefer grasslands, mountains, sandy pine forest, or swamps. Different snakes are adapted for different environments.

I have created this guide primarily for those who know little or nothing about snakes, but it will probably also appeal to diehard reptile enthusiasts. In each chapter I have tried to include such important data as pattern characteristics, sizes, number of young (brood size), range of occupation, prey, favored habitat, legal status, and even a little history behind when and who first described each species and subspecies. In addition, I provided a selection of excellent photos of each of these species for easy identification. In doing so, I hope this information will give you a better understanding and appreciation of these much-maligned creatures.

Area of Coverage

This new Guide covers all species of harmless snakes (non-venomous or not dangerous to humans) found in the western United States. The area of coverage includes the states of California, Oregon, Washington, Idaho, Nevada, Arizona, Utah, Wyoming, Montana, Colorado, New Mexico, Texas, Oklahoma, Kansas, Nebraska, South Dakota, and North Dakota. You will even find a few Eastern species included, as long as their ranges extend into the states covered.

Area Covered by this book shown in Green.

Range Maps

The 76 Range Maps presented are reasonable approximations of ranges for species and subspecies based on specimens and habitat preference. They are not exact boundaries, as no one knows the exact point where one subspecies ends and another begins, or even the exact range of any species. The maps are an overall picture of where certain snakes exist, but most will not occupy all terrain within the shaded portion of the map. Habitat varies for each, and I have made few allowances for natural barriers, such as high mountains, lakes, unsuitable habitat, or urban areas. Instead, the textual description for each snake's habitat will narrow down the approximate preferences. Keep those areas in mind when travelling through any of the ranges depicted on the maps.

The maps were created from the author's personal experience and books (Hubbs, 2004 & 2009), or based on maps appearing in other publications, such as Stebbins (2003) or Conant & Collins (1998), or on various Internet herp atlases. Holycross (2006) was extremely helpful in generating more detailed maps for certain species in Arizona, as were personal communications from amateur and professional herpetologists all over the west.

The area of coverage is in light green, while the areas not covered—the eastern U.S., Canada and Mexico—are shown in cream. Various colors shading the range of the snakes are found on the maps. Map captions designate the color representing each species or subspecies and intergrade zones where two subspecies blend as they change from one to the other. Question marks (?) indicate areas where a species may be present, but has not been sufficiently documented to be recognized on the maps.

The Eastern species covered in this book are treated just like the Western species, although most of the maps for those will only show their range in the states covered by this guide, as well as a small portion within the bordering states, Mexico, and Canada if applicable. Abbreviations for state names, like AZ for Arizona, are found on all maps for states in which the given species or subspecies occurs.

Genus, Species, Common, & Scientific Names

This book describes 95 species, each grouped by type. For example, there are six species of Garter Snakes that live in close association to water, so all of those can be found in the Aquatic Garter Snake chapter, along with their subspecies, if any. However, only one of the species is actually called the Aquatic Garter Snake, and I have simply lumped the other five into that category due to their extreme aquatic habits. Some chapters might be dedicated to one species and several subspecies, while others will contain multiple species and sometimes even Genera (the plural of genus). Put simply, "Genus" means a class of things that have common characteristics and that can be divided into subordinate kinds. The "subordinate kinds" are species and subspecies. These designations are used to classify or separate different kinds of animals, such as snakes. Snakes belong to a large Class of animals called Reptilia. Reptilia, in turn, is broken down into Orders, and then Families, which are further broken down into Genera, Species, and Subspecies if necessary. This book will only deal with the last three classifications, and those will only be seen in the scientific names of the snakes described. Just remember that the first name is the Genus, the second name is the Species, and the third (if any) is the Subspecies. Here's an example from one of the western snakes:

The California Kingsnake – *Lampropeltis getula californiae*
        Lampropeltis (Genus) *getula* (Species) *californiae* (Subspecies)

In the scientific name, the Genus is always capitalized, but not the species or subspecies name, and scientific names should always be written in italics.

Snakes have two names, a common name and a scientific name. The common name describes the species in English, i.e., Gopher Snake or Kingsnake. There can be many common names for the same animal, depending on how it is known in a local area or region, and I have tried to include as many as possible. The scientific name is the "official" name used by biologists, and is generally derived from Latin or Greek origins. Sometimes the scientific species or subspecies name will reflect the name of its discoverer or simply honor a herpetologist for their accomplishments. An example of the latter would be *Tantilla hobartsmithi* (Southwestern Black-headed Snake), which honors Hobart M. Smith.

The world of herpetology is constantly changing with regard to descriptions and reclassifications of animals. Many of the old, established common and scientific names for species and subspecies have changed over the past few years. Some of the changes are reflected here, but others are either very new and have not withstood the test of time, or are not accepted by a majority of publications. For those reasons I have chosen to use the older names for many species. I feel that the selection of names used here best describe the animals and their relationships to each other. At least one common name, Chaparral Whipsnake, was taken from Stebbins (2003) as I also believe this is a better name than the current, "Striped Racer."

Chapter Information

Chapters are arranged with Blind Snakes and Boas listed first, followed by an alphabetical listing of all others by genera and species. For example, the Bull Snake, Gopher Snakes, and Pine Snake are all found in the same group under *Pituophis*. The Ratsnakes and Foxsnakes are found under *Pantherophis*, but also include *Bogertophis* & *Senticolis*, so not everything is alphabetical, but can still be found fairly quickly, especially if the Table of Contents is utilized. The information in each chapter is broken down into several categories, and these may or may not include the following: Genera (if more than one genus name is included in a chapter), Species (if one or more species names are included in a chapter), Subspecies (if subspecies are included in the chapter), History, Other Common Names, Size, Identification, Brood Size, Range, Prey, Habitat, and Notes. These sections are explained below:

1. Genera, Species, and Subspecies will tell you the Common and Scientific names for each genus, species, and subspecies covered in that chapter.

2. History will explain who described the genus or species, when it was described, and possibly any changes in the scientific name.
3. Other Common Names lists alternate names by which the snake was either once known or is still known in various regions of the country.
4. Size gives the currently known average minimum and maximum, and often record lengths, for adults of each species discussed. Sizes are assigned to three categories: Small, Medium, and Large, with the lengths in inches and centimeters for the total length of the snake.
5. Identification describes what the snake looks like (although color photos are also provided for most).
6. Brood Size describes how many eggs or live young the snake may have, and often when birth or egg deposit occurs.
7. Range describes briefly where the species or subspecies are found within the United States. The Range Maps will make this information even easier to understand.
8. Prey refers to what the serpent eats.
9. Habitat describes the preferred terrain in which the snake may be found, as well as elevation minimum and maximum when known or applicable.
10. Notes contains extra information, including possible natural history, anecdotal stories, legal status, or trivia about each species.

What Are Snakes?

Everyone in the United States has probably heard of snakes. They are slender, legless, scaly reptiles without eyelids. They live underground, and occasionally or regularly move about on the surface, depending on the species. They can be found almost everywhere in temperate or tropical climates. Snakes come in many different colors and patterns. Some are colored to blend in to their environment, while others are almost outlandish in appearance and easily recognized.

Many people know the difference between harmless and venomous species, and if they don't, they should. Venomous snakes use toxic venom (poison) to subdue and kill prey items. If you are bitten, some can make you sick and some can actually cause death. Those snakes were covered in my previous book, *A Guide to the Rattlesnakes and other Venomous Serpents of the United States*, co-authored with Brendan O'Connor. It illustrates and describes the 42 different venomous snakes found in the United States. However, this book is not about dangerous snakes, it is about the harmless varieties. It is a companion to the other book. I hope it will give you some insight into, and understanding of, the various species that live in the western U.S., some of which might even be in your yard.

Benefits of Snakes

Snakes are nature's roto-rooters. Ever wonder why a plumber has a tool called a "snake"? Their bodies are designed to crawl into underground burrows, tunnels, and narrow crevices to control rodent populations and other creatures that might become a nuisance if allowed to over-populate. Many can be found occupying the same habitat and same region, but each has its own specialty when it comes to doing its job, which is helping to control other species of animals so they do not cause environmental problems.

Some snakes are excellent swimmers, and water snakes and garter snakes cull slow and dying fish from streams, ponds, and lakes. They also control the amphibian population, such as frogs and toads. Other snakes eat insects or rodents. Each has a specific list of prey items it instinctively seeks. However, snakes are also controlled. They are preyed upon by larger predators, such as hawks, owls, certain mammals (including some humans), large fish, and even other snakes. It is a process by which nature tries to stay in balance. For no other reason, snakes should be conserved and allowed to exist in the wild wherever they are found.

Types of Harmless Snakes

There are many different types of harmless snakes in the western United States. Some are small, while others are large in size, and each has its preferred habitat and favored prey. Despite size, snakes basically fall into two categories – those that live around water and prey on aquatic species, and those that are terrestrial and prey on terrestrial species. The aquatic species generally include Garter Snakes, Water Snakes, and Mud Snakes. Some of the more well-known terrestrial species include Gopher Snakes, King Snakes, Boas, Rat Snakes, Racers, and Ring-necked Snakes. There are many more terrestrial species than aquatic species, and each species in this book will be designated as either aquatic or terrestrial. However, sometimes a species will be both, as in the Terrestrial and Common Garter Snakes. Those live primarily on land, but are strongly tied to aquatic areas where they will prey on aquatic species as well as terrestrial species. These could be referred to as generalists as far as habitat and prey are concerned.

Snake Bite

Most of the serpents covered by this book are completely harmless, inoffensive, and will not bite a human unless extremely provoked. Those with a more irascible personality, such as Water Snakes, Rat Snakes, and Bull Snakes, will seldom hesitate to inflict a bite on anything they feel might be a threat, and that includes hands and arms within reach. However, the bites, while perhaps painful, are no more dangerous than a scrape or cut. Some snakes are so small they cannot even break the skin when they bite. Others will almost never attempt to bite, or if so, never connect on the strike. The Hog-nosed Snakes are some that fall into this category. Their strikes are more of a bluff, and intended to frighten rather than do harm. If you fear being bitten do not pick up or tease a snake. Leave them alone and they will leave you alone. This book does not encourage anyone to capture any snake, but if you happen to be bitten by one of the larger, more aggressive harmless species, you should treat the wound as if it were a cut or scrape and apply anti-infection ointment and bandaging as necessary.

Protection of Species

Some of the species covered in this book are protected by certain states and/or the federal government from collection or harassment. There are several reasons for such protections. 1) The species has lost so much of its original habitat that it is now listed as a threatened or endangered species and needs protection. 2) The species range barely extends into certain states and is protected to conserve whatever population is present. 3) The species is secretive and little is known of its true abundance, so it is protected as a measure of precaution. In addition, more than one of these reasons may exist for some species. I have tried to report the protected status of species in each chapter, where applicable, but this information may not be complete or up-to-date. If you desire to collect a snake for a pet, check with your state regulations before you do. You will not want to be fined for breaking the law, especially when it comes to threatened or endangered species that carry a penalty of up to $50,000.

The Narrow-headed Garter Snake (*Thamnophis rufipuntatus*) [shown here] found in Arizona & New Mexico will likely become one of the next federally protected Endangered Species due to non-native introduced frogs, crayfish, and fish that prey on the baby snakes. These introduced pests have severely lowered the populations of these snakes, or wiped them out completely, over much of the serpent's range.
Photo: Sam Murray

Desert Blind Snake (*Rena humilis cahuilae*). Photo: Sam Murray

Blind Snake
(Threadsnake)
Rena dissectus, Rena humilis, & Rena dulcis
Utah Blind Snake (*Rena humilis utahensis*) is Protected by law in UT
New Mexico Blind Snake (*Rena dissectus*) is Protected by law in CO & KS

Species & Subspecies: The New Mexico Blind Snake (*Rena dissectus*), Western Blind Snake (*Rena humilis*), & Texas Blind Snake (*Rena dulcis*). Two species contain subspecies:
Western Blind Snake: Southwestern Blind Snake (*Rena humilis humilis*) Baird & Girard, 1853; Desert Blind Snake (*Rena humilis cahuilae*) Klauber, 1931; Trans-Pecos Blind Snake (*Rena humilis segregus*) Klauber, 1939; Utah Blind Snake (*Rena humilis utahensis*) Tanner, 1938.
Texas Blind Snake: Texas Blind Snake (*Rena dulcis dulcis*) Baird & Girard, 1853; South Texas Blind Snake (*Rena dulcis rubellum*) Garman, 1884.
History: The Western & Texas Blind Snakes were first described by Spencer Fullerton Baird and Charles Frédéric Girard in 1853, while the New Mexico Blind Snake was described by Edward Cope in 1896. The names following the subspecies are those who first described each, along with the date of publication. This type of listing will be found for each species in this book.

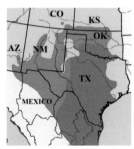
Left: New Mexico Blind Snake (*Rena dissectus*) (Red) & Texas Blind Snake (*Rena dulcis*) (Blue).

Right: Western Blind Snake (*Rena humilis)* Range.

Other Common Names: Brown Blind Snake, California Blind Snake, California Rena, California Worm Snake, Humble Sheep Snake, Sheep-nosed Snake, Threadsnakes, New Mexico Threadsnake, Southwestern Threadsnake, Western Slender Blind Snake, Western Threadsnake, Texas Slender Blind Snake, Texas Threadsnake, South Texas Threadsnake, Burrowing Snake, Worm Snake, Texas Rena, New Mexican Worm Snake, and Tanner's Blind Snake.

Size: Very Small. Western Blind Snake adults range in size from 7–16 in. (18–41 cm), while the Texas Blind Snake is even smaller, ranging from 5–11½ in. (12.7–28 cm). Record–13⅛ in. (33.3 cm).

Identification: A tiny, slender, cylindrical, silvery or pinkish purple or tan snake, with a blunt snout and tiny black dots for eyes. The eyes are basically vestigial, as this snake has no real use for vision due to its extreme subterranean habits. Blind snakes greatly resemble earthworms, and if not looked at closely may be mistaken for worms. A small spine can be found on the tip of the tail. These snakes are all similar in appearance, so the species and subspecies have been separated by differences in scale arrangement on the heads. The differences in species are as follows: The Western Blind Snake has one scale on top of the head between the ocular scales (those that contain the eyes), while the Texas and New Mexico Blind Snakes normally have three scales between the oculars. Other morphological differences separate the subspecies.

Brood Size: Egg-layer. Clutches range from 2–7 eggs.

Range: The Western Blind Snake is found in southern California and Baja California, the lower portion of the eastern Sierra, southern Nevada, extreme southwestern Utah, southern and central Arizona through southern New Mexico and the Big Bend region of Texas, and south into Mexico. The New Mexico Blind Snake's range includes southeast Arizona, the Rio Grande Valley in New Mexico, and southern and eastern New Mexico, western Texas to southwestern Kansas, extreme southeastern Colorado and western Oklahoma. The Texas Blind Snake occupies central Texas and the southern portion of Oklahoma, south into Mexico.

Prey: Small insects, such as ants, ant larvae, ant eggs, and termites.

Habitat: Terrestrial-Fossorial. Found from below sea level in the lower desert areas to 6,800 ft. (2,100 m). Habitat includes beaches and dunes, desert, prairies, chaparral, canyons, juniper forest, and grassland. It is especially fond of loose soils for burrowing, but can be found in harder soils as well.

Notes: Worldwide there are now 120 species of Blind Snakes, but only three are found in the western U.S. This secretive snake is seldom seen. It spends most of its life underground, only occasionally surfacing at night or to take refuge under a surface object when the soil is moist. I encountered my first Western Blind Snake in 1968 in Santa Clarita, California. My family had just moved into a new home near Soledad Canyon, and one of my first priorities was to climb the partially chaparral covered hillside that bordered our backyard. A family friend accompanied me to the top of the hill. He lifted the first rock he could find and discovered a Blind Snake. This experience was misleading however, as every Blind Snake I have seen since were found on roads at night.

Northern Rubber Boa (*Charina bottae*). Photo: Alan St. John

Rubber Boa

Charina bottae & *Charina umbratica*
Southern Rubber Boa (*Charina umbratica*) is Protected by law in CA

Species: At this time there are two species of Rubber Boas, the Northern Rubber Boa (*Charina bottae*) and the Southern Rubber Boa (*Charina umbratica*). In the past, the Southern Rubber Boa was considered a subspecies of *Charina bottae*, and then elevated to full species status. It may again find itself in the subspecies category or simply absorbed into the *Charina bottae* species due to ongoing DNA and morphological analysis. Current information apparently demonstrates that the differences between the two species are not as significant as once thought.

History: The Northern Rubber Boa (*Charina bottae*) was described by H.M.D. de Blainville in 1835, while the Southern Rubber Boa (*Charina umbratica*) was described by Lawrence Klauber in 1943.

Other Common Names: Boa, Rubber Snake, Pacific Rubber Boa, Pacific Rubber Snake, Great Basin Rubber Boa, Great Basin Rubber Snake, Lead-colored Worm Snake, Silver Snake, Two-headed Snake, Wood Snake, Botta's Worm Snake, Northern Rubber boa, and Worm Snake.

Size: Small to medium, adults are 18–33 in. (45.7–84 cm). The Southern Rubber Boa is considered a dwarf race, generally attaining smaller lengths than its northern counterpart, but not really noticeable to the casual observer.

N. Rubber Boa (*Charina bottae*) (Blue) and S. Rubber Boa (*Charina umbratica*) (Red).

Identification: Smooth-scaled. A stout-bodied beige, tan, pinkish, brownish, or greenish smooth-scaled snake, with vertically oval pupils, that looks like rubber due to the way its skin folds when the body is curved or bent. The young are light tan or pinkish tan in color (sometimes brilliant pink), darkening with age. Belly generally has dark flecks or mottling of brown, orange, or black. Like the Rosy Boa, anal spurs are usually present on males, and small or absent on females. Tip of tail is blunt.

Brood Size: Live-bearing. A brood can consist of 2–8 young, born generally from August to November.

Range: Found primarily from the mountains of southern California (San Bernardino & San Jacinto) north to southern British Columbia and Alberta, within the Coast, Sierra Nevada, and Cascade mountain ranges, east through most of Oregon and Washington, all of Idaho, northern Nevada, western Montana, northwestern Wyoming, and the Wasatch and Uinta Ranges in Utah. May also be present in extreme northwestern Colorado.

Prey: Primarily small rodents and their young, but will also take small birds, reptiles (lizards and snakes), and amphibians (salamanders). The Southern Rubber Boa especially likes Sagebrush Lizards (*Sceloporus graciosus*).

Habitat: Terrestrial. Found from sea-level to over 10,000 ft. (3,050 m), this snake is most often associated with pine forest, forest edge, mountain slopes, rocky canyons, chaparral, mountain meadows, and grassland. Water is not a necessary component of Rubber Boa habitat, as these fossorial snakes receive most of their moisture intake from the prey they consume. Prefers soft soil for burrowing, but also utilizes rodent tunnels for refuge and searching for prey.

Notes: Constrictors. When threatened, often rolls into a ball, exposing its blunt tail to the predator, while keeping the head concealed within its coils. Often active during cold temperatures (mid-50s). The Northern Rubber Boa is a long-lived snake, and some may exceed 40 years of age in the wild. Like the Rosy Boa (described next), this is an abundant, slow, docile creature. Its habitat is extensive, most of which lies within the boundaries of national forests, large ranches, and parklands, secure from the prospect of future development or habitat destruction. The Southern Rubber Boa is also abundant where it occurs, but due to its smaller range compared to the Northern Rubber Boa, it is currently considered a Threatened Species and may not be collected.

Southern Rubber Boa (*Charina umbratica*).
Photo: Gary Nafis

Coastal Rosy Boa (*Lichanura trivirgata roseofusca*) from
Los Angeles County, CA.   Photo: Brian Hubbs

Rosy Boa

(Three-Lined Boa)

Lichanura trivirgata

Desert Rosy Boa (*L. t. gracia*) is protected by law in NV

Species & Subspecies: One species and three subspecies of Rosy Boa (*Lichanura trivirgata*) are found in the western U.S.:
Mexican Rosy Boa (*Lichanura trivirgata trivirgata*) Cope, 1861; Coastal Rosy Boa (*Lichanura trivirgata roseofusca*) Cope, 1868; and Desert Rosy Boa (*Lichanura trivirgata gracia*) Klauber, 1931.

History: What is now known as the Mexican Rosy Boa (*Lichanura trivigata trivirgata*) was first described by Edward D. Cope in 1861. He later described the Coastal subspecies (*Lichanura trivigata roseofusca*) in 1868, and in 1931 Lawrence Klauber described the Desert subspecies (*Lichanura trivigata gracia*). The common name refers to the rosy ventral (belly) coloration on some individuals, and continues to cause confusion among non-herpetologists, some of which mistake any reddish snake for a Rosy Boa, including Coachwhips (*Masticophis flagellum*). Edward Cope originally gave the common name of Three-Lined Boa to this species, and this might be a more appropriate name from a descriptive standpoint.

Range of Rosy Boa (*Lichanura trivirgata*). Coastal (Green), Desert (Red), & Mexican (Blue).

Other Common Names: California Boa, California Rosy Boa, Many Scaled Boa, Two-headed Snake, and Three-lined Boa.

Size: A medium-sized snake that ranges from 17–50 in. (43–127 cm) in adults. Newborns are about 12 in. (30 cm) at birth.

Identification: Smooth-scaled and stout-bodied, like the Rubber Boa (See previous account), but with a silvery gray, tan, brown, steel blue, cream, whitish, or yellowish ground color that is broken by three lengthwise stripes (one down the center of the back and one on each side) of orange, reddish, brown, chocolate, or nearly black, depending on location and subspecies. The Mexican Rosy Boa has the darkest stripes, which are usually dark chocolate to nearly black. The Coastal Rosy Boa has jagged, irregular stripes or no visible stripes at all. The other two subspecies have fairly straight and evenly defined stripes, and are usually associated with desert habitats. In extreme southern San Diego County, California there is a color pattern of the Coastal Rosy Boa that is almost solid brown, with no stripes visible (Uncolored morph). Like the Rubber Boa, anal spurs are usually present on males and small or absent on females.

Brood Size: Live-bearing. A brood can consist of 3–14 young, born generally from October to November.

Range: The Coastal Rosy Boa is found from the western end of the San Gabriel and Sierra Pelona Mountains in Los Angeles County southeast through the lower elevations of the San Bernardino and San Jacinto Mountains, Chino Hills, Riverside-Hemet-Temecula region, and chaparral areas and Peninsula Range of San Diego County into northern Baja California, Mexico. Intergrades with the Desert Rosy Boa are found in the San Gorgonio Pass region and western foothills of the Little San Bernardino Mountains. Rumors of Rosy Boas in the Santa Monica and Santa Susana Mountains have not been verified.

The Desert Rosy Boa is found in the hills and mountains of the Mohave and Colorado Deserts in California, and also western Arizona, from the Cerbat Mountains south and eastward to the vicinity of Gila Bend and Yuma. Rumors have persisted for years of Rosy Boas occurring in extreme southern Nevada, and recently one from that area has been deposited in a museum. Those rumored boas were never proven to exist (by actual specimen or photo voucher) for fear the state would immediately protect the snake from collecting. Evidently the fears were well founded, as that is exactly what happened as soon as the specimen was written up in a scientific journal. I am amazed at how quickly some game agencies move to make a species off-limits or declared "endangered" based on new state records, especially before a second example could be found or any study of population density carried out. It is ludicrous to believe the Nevada population could be in any jeopardy. It is found in a very rugged and undeveloped mountain range. In fact, the area has only one main dirt road.

The Mexican Rosy Boa reaches its most northerly locality in the Maricopa Mountains (and Estrella Mountains?) of Maricopa County, Arizona. The range then extends southwest and southeast through the Organ Pipe Cactus National Monument area and Tohono-O'odham Indian Reservation into northern and western Sonora, Mexico.

Prey: Primarily small rodents and their young, but will also take small birds, and occasionally even reptiles and amphibians.

Habitat: Terrestrial. Found from sea-level to around 5,000 feet (1,524 m) in California, and possibly higher in the San Gabriel Mountains of southern California, based on an unverified sight record from 6,790 feet (2,070 m). Found to about 5,600 feet (1,707 m) in Arizona. Rocky hillsides, canyons, chaparral, and washes are the primary habitats. These snakes are very fossorial, spending much of their time underground or within rock crevices.

Like all other desert dwellers, water is not a necessary component of their habitat.

Notes: Constrictors. An extremely common species, Rosy Boas are one of the most abundant snakes in southern California. Some people still believe they are un-common, because they are seldom seen due to their fossorial habits, but those who know how to look for them realize the depth of their occupation and enormity of their numerical abundance. In prime habitat, where extensive rocky cover and rodent prey exists, these snakes can number over 30 per acre. It is estimated by some experts that the California population alone exceeds 5 million.

Like most snake species, Rosy Boas have specific activity periods above and below ground. During certain times of the year they can be seen crossing road surfaces at night or during the late afternoon or morning hours. Many amateur herpetologists search for them in this manner, as they make desirable pets due to their docile nature. Rosy Boas seldom move quickly, except when trying to secure a meal. There is an old joke that goes, "When you find a Rosy Boa on the road, you have time to go to the store and get a soda because the snake will still be there when you get back." While this is a gross exaggeration, it is true that Rosy Boas are very, very slow at escaping. In southern California, one road is so popular among Rosy Boa enthusiasts that the California Department of Fish & Wildlife (DF&W) has a game warden lurking in the area during the peak collecting season, to insure that collectors have a valid fishing license (required for the collection of any non-venomous California reptile or amphibian). Many would-be collectors have been fooled into stopping for his colorful ropes and planted "road-killed" snakes, and those without licenses are issued a ticket to appear at the nearest courthouse. While this may help enforce license regulations, it has no conservation value for protecting the species because road collecting has been shown to be a sustained-yield harvest and has no effect on the overall population in that area. Field notes from various collectors have shown that Rosy Boas are no more common or scarce on that road today than they were in the 1950s. This is because a road is just a thin line through a vast amount of surrounding habitat, and new boas are produced every year through reproduction.

Coastal Rosy Boa
(*Lichanura trivirgata roseofusca*) from Riverside County, CA.

Photo: Brian Hinds

Coastal Rosy Boa
(*Lichanura trivirgata roseofusca*) (Unicolor Morph) from San Diego County, CA.

Photo: Brian Hinds

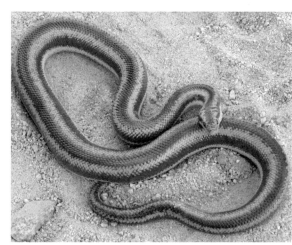

Desert Rosy Boa
(*Lichanura trivirgata gracia*) from California.

Photo: Brian Hinds

Mexican Rosy Boa
(*Lichanura trivirgata trivirgata*) from Arizona.

Photo: Brian Hinds

Painted Desert Glossy Snake (*Arizona elegans philipi*).
Photo: Brian Hubbs

Glossy Snake
Arizona elegans
Protected by law in CO, KS, & UT

Species & Subspecies: The Glossy Snake (*Arizona elegans*) consists of seven subspecies:

Texas Glossy Snake (*Arizona elegans arenicola*) Dixon, 1960
Kansas Glossy Snake (*Arizona elegans elegans*) Kennicott, 1859
Mojave Glossy Snake (*Arizona elegans candida*) Klauber, 1946
Desert Glossy Snake (*Arizona elegans eburnata*) Klauber, 1946
Arizona Glossy Snake (*Arizona elegans noctivaga*) Klauber, 1946
California Glossy Snake (*Arizona elegans occidentalis*) Blanchard, 1924
Painted Desert Glossy Snake (*Arizona elegans philipi*) Klauber, 1946.

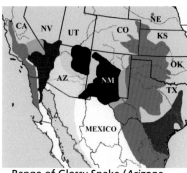
Range of Glossy Snake (*Arizona elegans*). California (Blue), Mojave (Light Green), Desert (Maroon), Arizona (Yellow), Painted Desert (Black), Kansas (Dark Green), Texas (Red), and Intergrade zone (Gray).

History: The Glossy Snake was first described by Robert Kennicott in 1859. The different subspecies were described in the years noted and by the persons whose names follow the scientific names in the list above.

Other Common Names: Arizona Snake, Elegant Bull Snake, Faded Snake, Slender Gopher Snake, and Sand Snake.

Size: Medium to large. Adults average 26–36 in. (66–91 cm) in length, but the record size is 70 in. (178 cm). Juveniles are generally 9½–11 in. (24–28 cm) at hatching.

Identification: Smooth-scaled. Similar to the Gopher Snake (Pituophis), but generally smaller and having a more reduced pattern of 39–85 (depending on subspecies) transverse (tilted crosswise) tan, brown, gray, or reddish blotches that are lightly edged in black on a tan, yellowish, or light brown background. The belly is solid white or light tan. These snakes were once called the "Faded Snake" due to bleached appearance of their pattern, which becomes more obscured with age. Occasionally the blotches merge and form a partial or full lengthwise stripe.

Brood Size: Egg layer. A clutch of 3–24 eggs (average 5–12) are usually laid from June to July.

Range: This is a wide-ranging serpent, found from coastal and inland California and Baja California, Mexico to southern Kansas and southeastern Texas, on into mainland Mexico.

Prey: Chiefly lizards, but also small rodents, birds, and snakes are consumed.

Habitat: Terrestrial. Below sea-level to around 7,200 feet (2,195 m). Sandy to gravelly desert, sandy riverbeds and washes, desert grassland, alluvial fans, canyon bottoms, and scrub brush are all inhabited by this species.

Notes: Constrictors. Most subspecies are common to abundant. Glossy Snakes are excellent burrowers, and seldom seen due to their nocturnal and crepuscular habits. Most live in arid places and only venture abroad at night. They can be commonly seen on desert roadways that traverse their preferred habitat after dark, as well as within sandy grassland and dune habitats. Occasionally they can be found during the day beneath surface debris if the conditions are not dry. In the eastern part of the range they are more active during daylight hours. I search for snakes quite frequently, and have only seen Glossy Snakes during the day on two occasions, either crawling at dusk or beneath surface trash. One subspecies may be in trouble, at least within its coastal range, the California Glossy Snake has lost a large portion of its habitat to urban development in Los Angeles, Orange, Riverside, and San Diego counties.

California Glossy Snake (*Arizona elegans occidentalis*).

Photo: Gary Nafis

Texas Glossy Snake (*Arizona elegans arenicola*).

Photo: Brian Hubbs

Western Worm Snake (*Carphophis vermis*).
Photo: Brian Hubbs

Worm Snake
Carphophis vermis

Species: There is one species of Worm Snake that occurs within the area covered by this book, the Western Worm Snake (*Carphophis vermis*).

History: The genus *Carphophis* was first described by Paul Gervais in 1843, while the species *Carphophis vermis* was described by Robert Kennicott in 1859.

Other Common Names: Blind Worm, Ground Snake, Twig Snake, Western Twig Snake, Cricket Snake, Little Red Snake, and Thunder Snake.

Size: Very small. Adults average 7½–11 in. (19–28 cm), with a record size of 15⅜ in. (39.1 cm). Young hatch at about 4 in. (10 cm).

Identification: Smooth-scaled. This is a two-toned, purplish brown or black snake with a pinkish red belly that extends up the sides for about three scale rows.

Brood Size: Egg-layer. From 2–8 eggs are laid in late June or early July. Hatching generally occurs in August or early September.

Range: The Western worm Snake is found in extreme northeast Texas, most of eastern Oklahoma, the eastern quarter of Kansas, and southeastern Nebraska, and then eastward across most of Missouri, extreme southern Iowa and west-central Illinois, and the western two-thirds of Arkansas. Isolated populations in northeastern Louisiana.

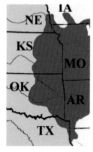

Prey: Earthworms and other soft-bodied insects.

Habitat: Terrestrial. Woodlands, edge of woodland, leaf litter, grasslands next to woodlands, edge of marshes, gardens, riparian corridors, glades, and old rock walls. From the lowlands of the Mississippi Valley to the tops of the Ozark Mountains.

Notes: This is an extremely abundant snake where it occurs. A burrower, it spends most of its life underground or under objects with moist soil beneath.

Texas Scarlet Snake (*Cemophora coccinea lineri*).
Photo: Troy Hibbitts

Scarletsnake

Cemophora coccinea
Protected by law in TX

Species & Subspecies: The Scarletsnake (*Cemophora coccinea*) has two subspecies occurring within the area covered by this book: The Texas Scarletsnake (*Cemophora coccinea lineri*) Williams, Brown, and Wilson, 1966 and the Northern Scarletsnake (*Cemophora coccinea copei*) Jan, 1863.

History: The Scarletsnake (*Cemophora coccinea*) was described by Johann Friedrich Blumenbach in 1788 as *Coluber coccineus*, which was later changed to [Cemophora coccinea] by Edward Cope in 1860.

Other Common Names: False Coral Snake and Scarlet Snake.

Size: A small to medium sized snake. Adults average 14–20 in. (36–51 cm) in length, but the record size is 32 ½ in. (83 cm). Young are usually 5–7 in. (12.5–17.78 cm) at hatching.

Identification: Smooth-scaled. There are generally 17-24 red rings or blotches bordered by black, which in turn are bordered by yellow, tan, or whitish rings down the back (dorsum). The snout is reddish. The Scarletsnake is very similar in appearance to the Scarlet Kingsnake (not found in the West); however, it differs in having a plain colored belly of light gray, yellowish, or whitish. Texas Scarletsnakes have less brilliant red blotches with no black along their lower edges.

Range of Scarletsnake (*Cemophora coccinea*). Texas (Blue) & Northern (Red).

Brood Size: Egg-layer. Generally 3–8 eggs are laid during the summer, which hatch in late summer or fall.

Range: The Texas Scarletsnake is found in southeastern Texas on the coast and a little inland, from approximately 50 miles north of Corpus Christie to just north of Brownsville, and then westward in the northern area of the "Valley" (See Range map). The Northern Scarletsnake is found east and north of Houston in eastern and northeastern Texas, the eastern half of Oklahoma, then east through most of Arkansas, northwestern and northern Louisiana, across the southern states (except peninsular Florida) and through most of the eastern coastal states to southern New Jersey. It also occurs over most of Tennessee and Kentucky, and in a small section of central Missouri.

Prey: This snake primarily eats lizards and reptile eggs, but also are known to take small mice and other snakes, however these snakes seldom eat in captivity and make poor captives.

Habitat: Terrestrial. Very fossorial and a good burrower. It tends to favor sandy or loamy soil within its range. When on the surface, it takes refuge beneath or inside rotting logs, bark, rocks, etc. Indeed, my first and only Scarletsnake was found inside a rotting log as I searched for snakes in south-central Georgia.

Notes: Constrictors. The Scarletsnake has enlarged posterior (rear) maxillary (upper) teeth that are used to pierce the shell of eggs. Due to the coloration, this snake could possibly be confused with the venomous Coral Snake, but the red snout is an easy distinction between the two. The Coral Snake has a black snout (See my *Guide to the Rattlesnakes and other Venomous Serpents of the United States*).

Northern Scarletsnake (*Cemophora concinea*).
Photo: Bill Love

Variable Sandsnake (*Chilomeniscus stramineus*).
Photo: Ben Jones

Variable Sandsnake
Chilomeniscus stramineus

Species & History: There is one Sandsnake species in the western U.S., the Variable Sandsnake (*Chilomeniscus stramineus*). It was first described by Edward Cope in 1860.
Other Common Names: Banded Sandsnake and Western Sandsnake
Size: Very Small. Adults range from 7–11 in. (18–28 cm).
Identification: Smooth-scaled. Sandsnakes are similar to Shovel-nosed Snakes, but their body is stouter. There are generally 19–49 black crossbands on a ground color of pale yellow, reddish orange, or yellowish cinnamon, often with the upper most part of the back (dorsum) being orange between the black bands. The snout is light colored and there is a black band across the eyes and top of head. The belly is dull yellow or whitish. There is a unicolored version of this snake that occurs in the cape region of Baja California Sur, Mexico.
Brood Size: Egg layer. From 2–4 eggs, laid from June to August.
Range: From southwestern (two localities) and south-central Arizona south into western Sonora, Mexico. Also found throughout most of Baja California, Mexico, except for the extreme northern and northeastern parts. This snake may possibly occur in southeastern California, west of the Colorado River, as there have been unconfirmed reports from the Algodones Dunes area.
Prey: Eats ants and their pupae, centipedes, roaches, small grasshoppers, and other small insects.
Habitat: Terrestrial. Sea-level to around 3,000 feet (914 m). Prefers fine to coarse sand and leaf litter, such as washes, or in loamy soil. It can occur in open desert as well as canyons and washes in rocky terrain.
Notes: The Variable Sandsnake is even more extreme of a sand swimmer than the Shovel-nosed Snake (See next chapter). It is highly adapted for burrowing underground, and is seldom found on the surface, except at night. Due to the coloration, this snake could possibly be confused with the venomous Coral Snake, but the light snout is an easy distinction between the two. The Coral Snake has a black snout (See my *Guide to the Rattlesnakes and other Venomous Serpents of the United States*).

Colorado Desert Shovelnose (*Chionactis occipitalis annulata*).
Photo: David Jahn

Shovel-nosed Snakes
Chionactis occipitalis & xChionactis palarostris

Species & Subspecies: There are two species of Shovel-nosed Snakes in the western U.S., listed below with their five subspecies.

1) Western Shovel-nosed Snake (*Chionactis occipitalis*) Hallowell, 1854:
   Colorado Desert Shovel-nosed Snake (*Chionactis occipitalis annulata*) Baird, 1859
   Tucson Shovel-nosed Snake (*Chionactis occipitalis klauberi*) Stickel, 1941
   Mohave Shovel-nosed Snake (*Chionactis o. occipitalis*) Hallowell, 1854
   Nevada Shovel-nosed Snake (*Chionactis occipitalis talpina*) Klauber, 1951.
2) Sonoran Shovel-nosed Snake (*Chionactis palarostris*) Klauber, 1937:
   Organ Pipe Shovel-nosed Snake (*Chionactis palarostris organica*) Klauber, 1951.

History: The Western Shovel-nosed Snake was first described by Edward Hallowell in 1854, while the Sonoran Shovel-nosed Snake was described by Lawrence M. Klauber in 1937. Only the Organ Pipe subspecies of the Sonoran Shovel-nosed Snake occurs within the U.S.

Other Common Names: Banded Snake, Spade-nosed Snake, Desert Snake, Hallowell's Ground Snake, Mojave Ground Snake, Pencil Snake, Ringed Ground Snake, Shovelnose Snake, and Tricolored Ground Snake.

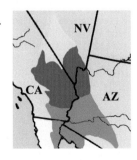

Ranges of Shovel-nosed Snakes.
Left: Organ Pipe Shovel-nosed
Right: Nevada Shovel-nosed
(Yellow), Mohave Shovel-nosed
(Blue), Colorado Desert Shovel-
nosed (Orange), and Tucson
Shovel-nosed (Green).

Size: Small. Adults range from 10–17 in. (25–43 cm).

Identification: Smooth-scaled. A whitish, cream, or pale yellow snake with 21 or more (20 or less in Sonoran Shovel-nosed Snake) alternating bands of red and black. The Sonoran Shovel-nosed Snake has wider bands than any of the others. On all, the black bands generally encircle the rear half of the body. The Mohave Shovel-nosed Snake usually lacks red bands. The snout is light, and there is a black "mask" across the eyes and head. The snout is slightly flattened, and gives the snake its common name.

Brood Size: Egg-layer. The Western Shovel-nosed Snake is known to have clutches of between 2–9 eggs in late spring and summer, with the Sonoran Shovel-nosed Snake laying up to 5 eggs during the same time frame.

Range: Shovel-nosed Snakes are primarily found in desert regions, from the Mohave and Colorado Deserts in the west to the Sonoran Desert in Arizona. Apparently absent today from much of the Tucson region due to destruction of its habitat by development and farming.

Prey: The Western Shovel-nosed Snake preys on invertebrates, including insects, spiders, centipedes, moth pupae, and scorpions. It may also eat reptile eggs.

Habitat: Terrestrial. Below sea-level to about 4,700 feet (1,430 m). These are desert dwellers, preferring the loose soil of washes, dunes, and flats, as well as rocky hillsides containing sandy gullies, but mostly found on level valley floors, alluvial fans, and in wide canyons. The Sonoran Shovel-nosed Snake prefers Palo Verde–Saguaro associations and is not as picky about sandy soil as is the Western Shovel-nosed Snake.

Notes: This is another abundant nocturnal and crepuscular (dusk) dweller of arid lands, seldom seen during the daylight hours, however, the Tucson Shovel-nosed Snake has lost a great deal of habitat to urbanization and farming. An excellent burrower, these snakes seem to swim through sand. Though they may have the same coloration and order of colors as the venomous Coral Snake (which has a solid black snout), these are tiny, harmless creatures. (See my *Guide to the Rattlesnakes and other Venomous Serpents of the United States*).

Mohave Shovelnose (*Chionactis occipitalis occipitalis*).
Photo: Ben Jones

Organ Pipe Shovelnose (*Chionactis palarostris organica*).
Photo: Brian Hubbs

Tucson Shovelnose (*Chionactis occipitalis klauberi*).
Photo: Ben Jones

Eastern Yellow-bellied Racer
(*Coluber constrictor flaviventris*)
Photo: Brian Hubbs

Northern Speckled Racer
(*Drymobius margaritiferus*).
Photo: Troy Hibbitts

Racers
Coluber constrictor & *Drymobius margaritiferus*
Speckled Racer (*Drymobius margaritiferus*) is Protected by law in TX

Genera, Species & Subspecies: Two species of racers from two genera are found in the western U.S (The Whipsnakes can be found in their own chapter under *Masticophis*). The two species and their subspecies are as follows:

1) The North American Racer (*Coluber constrictor*):
   Western Yellow-belied Racer (*Coluber constrictor mormon*) Baird & Girard, 1852
   Eastern Yellow-belied Racer (*Coluber constrictor flaviventris*) Say, 1823
   Buttermilk Racer (*Coluber constrictor anthicus*) Cope, 1862
   Tan Racer (*Coluber constrictor etheridgei*) Wilson, 1970
   Mexican Racer (*Coluber constrictor oaxaca*) Jan, 1863
   Southern Black Racer (*Coluber constrictor priapus*) Dunn and Wood, 1939
2) The Speckled Racer (*Drymobius margaritiferus*):
   Northern Speckled Racer (*Drymobius margaritiferus margaritiferus*) Schlegel, 1837.

History: The genus *Coluber* was first described by Carolus Linnaeus in 1758, while the species *Drymobius margaritiferus*was described by Hermann Schlegel in 1837.

Other Common Names: Regional and former common names for the various North American Racers include: Black Snake, Blue Chaser, Blue Racer,

Racer Ranges

Left: Speckled
Right: W. Yellow-bellied (Blue),
Eastern Yellow-belied (Green),
Mexican (Maroon),
Tan (Lavender),
Buttermilk (Orange), Southern Black (Yellow).

Blue Runner, Brown Racer, Chicken Snake, Go Fast Snake, Green Racer, Mormon Racer, Olive Racer, Pilot Snake, Spotted Racer, Variegated Racer, Western Blue Racer, White Oak Racer, Yellow-bellied Adder, Yellow-bellied Black Snake, and Yellow Coachwhip. Other common names for the Speckled Racer are: Green–spotted Racer, Schlegel's Snake, Speckled Ground Snake, and Mexican Speckled Snake.

Size: Medium to large. The North American Racers (*Coluber constrictor*) range in size from 20–75 in. (51–190 cm), but average around 36 in (91 cm). The Northern Speckled Racer averages 30–40 in. (76–102 cm), with a record size of 50 in. (127 cm).

Identification: Smooth-scaled. These are "Go-Fast" snakes, and they seldom sit still long enough for anyone to get a good look at them. The name racer is perfect, and these serpents can move at speeds of up to 5 mph, and usually not in a straight line, which only adds to the frustration of trying to keep up with them. Western and Eastern Yellow-belied Racers are greenish, gray, tan, olive, or even bluish in coloration, with yellow-to-cream bellies. Some can be light green and bright lemon yellow, especially in the Sand Hills region of Nebraska. The Buttermilk Racer is black, bluish, olive, or gray, with splotches of lighter color (as if it were bleached). No two look identical. The Mexican Racer is green or greenish-gray with lighter sides and a yellow or yellowish-green belly. The Tan Racer is similar to the Buttermilk Racer, but light tan above with fewer light spots. The Southern Black Racer is black above and on the belly. There is usually some white on the throat and chin. The Northern Speckled Racer looks different from all of these others, being black and bluish (part of each scale is blue and black) with a yellow spot in the center of each scale. The belly is plain yellow or white.

Brood Size: Egg-layers. North American Racer clutches range from 3–30 eggs. The Speckled Racer lays up to 8 eggs.

Range: The Racers (*Coluber constrictor*) range from coast to coast, except in the desert regions, highest areas of the Rocky Mountains, and most of Arizona. The Northern Speckled Racer is found in extreme southern Texas and south into Mexico. Mostly found south of the border, it exists in the U.S. at the northernmost end of its range.

Prey: Rodents, small birds, lizards, other snakes, frogs, and insects have allbeen documented to be eaten by these species.

Habitat: Terrestrial. Sea-level to around 8,300 feet (2,550 m). These snakes prefer open areas, from grasslands, sand hills, and plains, to the edges of swamps and lower elevations of mountainous regions. Around woodlands this is an edge inhabitant.

Notes: Racers are not only quick, they are good climbers. One warm spring day in the New Jersey Pine Barrens I accidently startled one of the eastern subspecies (Northern Black Racer) not covered in this book. I watched in amazement as it zoomed into a tree, gliding effortlessly from branch to branch as if the tree was an escalator. There it sat in the topmost branches, as if defying me to come after it. I didn't, but I photographed it as it rested. It was an event I had read about, but never witnessed.

Western Yellow-
belied Racer
(*Coluber constrictor
mormon*).
Photo: David Jahn

Western Yellow-belied
Racer Venter (*Coluber
constrictor mormon*).
Photo: Brian Hubbs

Buttermilk Racer
(*Coluber constrictor
anthicus*).
Photo: Troy Hibbitts

Tamaulipan Black-striped Snake (*Coniophanes imperialis imperialis*).
Photo: Brian Hubbs

Black-striped Snake

Coniophanes imperialis
Protected by law in TX
Mildly Venomous

Species & Subspecies: There is one species consisting of one subspecies of Black-striped Snake found in the western U.S., the Tamaulipan Black-striped Snake (*Coniophanes imperialis imperialis*) Baird, 1859.

History: The Black-striped Snake was first described by Spencer Fullerton Baird as *Taeniophis imperialis* in 1859, but the genus name was changed to *Coniophanes* by Edward Hallowell in 1860.

Other Common Names: Black-banded Snake, Red-bellied Snake, and Imperial Snake.

Size: Small. Adults are usually 12–18 in. (31–46 cm), with a record size of 20 in. (51 cm).

Identification: Smooth scaled. This snake is light brown or tan above, with a center stripe of dark brown or black, and sides of dark brown. The head is dark brown, with a light longitudinal stripe across the top of each eye that terminates before the neck begins. Bright orange or red below.

Brood Size: Egg-layer. Lays 2–10 eggs from April to June.

Range: Another primarily south of the border species, this snake reaches its northern limit in extreme south Texas.

Prey: Eats lizards, small snakes, small frogs and toads, and juvenile mice.

Habitat: Terrestrial. Found almost anywhere in the flat mesquite, scrub and grassy habitats north of the Rio Grande. It hides under debris, trash, and dead vegetation when the surface is moist.

Notes: While generally docile and reluctant to bite, this is a mildly venomous rear-fanged snake that can cause slight pain, swelling, and numbness to the bitten area in humans. The symptoms may last for several days, especially swelling. It is probably not a good idea to induce one of these snakes to bite. Abundant where found, but loss of historic habitat to farming and urban development have caused this species to be protected. The snake pictured in this chapter was found in south Texas just outside the city of Brownsville.

Common Sharp-tailed Snake (*Contia tenuis*). Photo: Alan St. John

Sharp-tailed Snakes
Contia tenuis & Contia longicaudae

Species: Sharp-tailed Snake (*Contia tenuis*) and Forest Sharp-tailed Snake (*Contia longicaudae*).

History: The Sharp-tailed Snake (*Contia tenuis*) was first described by Spencer Fullerton Baird and Charles Frédéric Girard in 1852, and the Forest Sharp-tailed Snake (*Contia longicaudae*) was formally described by Chris Feldman & Richard Hoyer in 2010.

Size: Small. Adults range from 12–18 in. (30–46 cm).

Identification: Smooth-scaled. Reddish-brown or gray above, typically with reddish or yellow upper side-stripe. Belly is light cream or gray, with a black crossbar on each scale. Tail has a sharp spine at the tip.

Brood Size: Egg-layers. A clutch of 2–8 eggs is laid from June to July.

Range: The Sharp-tailed Snake has a spotty range from Canada (Southeastern Vancouver Island) and Washington, through western Oregon south to northwestern California (to near Morro Bay) and Sierra Nevada Mountains (Blue area on map). The Forest Sharp-tail is found within the same range, only in more limited areas (see yellow area on map). In some places the two species occur together in the same habitat (shown on map as yellow with diagonal blue crossbars). The entire range of the Forest Sharp-tail has not been fully determined yet, and will undoubtedly be expanded in the future.

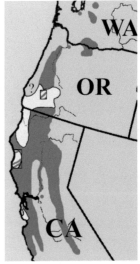

Prey: Slugs and their eggs, and occasionally Slender Salamanders.

Habitat: Terrestrial. Sea-level to around 6,600 feet (2,010 m). Depending on the location, Sharp-tailed Snakes can be found in open grassland, riparian zones, chaparral, wooded edge, and forest. The Forest Sharp-tailed Snake appears to prefer a more forested, humid environment.

Notes: The Forest Sharp-tailed Snake went undetected for over 150 years until Richard Hoyer noticed that there were differences in tail lengths and other specifics between it and the more common Sharp-tailed Snake (*Contia tenuis*). It has only been formally described since 2010, and in time will undoubtedly be found to have a much larger range than now known. Sharp-tailed Snakes are extremely abundant, which is expected due to their small size. Several amateur herpetologists I know have found dozens under a single discarded piece of plywood at the right time of year.

Forest Sharp-tailed Snake (*Contia longicaudae*). Photo: Alan St. John

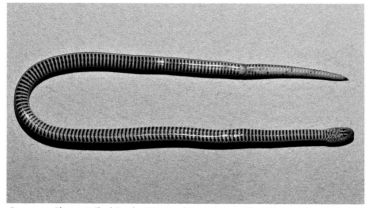

Common Sharp-tailed Snake Venter (*Contia tenuis*). Photo: Alan St. John

Coralbelly Ring-necked Snake (*D. p. pulchellus*). Photo: Brian Hubbs

Ring-necked Snake
Diadophis punctatus

Species & Subspecies: The Ring-necked Snake (*Diadophis punctatus*) has nine subspecies occurring within the scope of this book. They are:

Pacific Ring-necked Snake (*D. p. amabilis*) Baird & Girard, 1853
Prairie Ring-necked Snake (*D. p. arnyi*) Kennicott, 1858
San Bernardino Ring-necked Snake (*D. p. modestus*) Bocourt, 1886
Northwestern Ring-necked Snake (*D. p. occidentalis*) Blanchard, 1923
Coralbelly Ring-necked Snake (*D. p. pulchellus*) Baird & Girard, 1853
Regal Ring-necked Snake (*D. p. regalis*) Baird & Girard, 1853
San Diego Ring-necked Snake (*D. p. similis*) Blanchard, 1923
Mississippi Ring-necked Snake (*D. p. stictogenys*) Cope, 1860
Monterey Ring-necked Snake (*D. p. vandenburgii*) Blanchard, 1923

Ring-necked Ranges

NW (Gray), Pacific (Orange), Monterey (Light Blue), San Bernardino (Yellow), San Diego (Black), Coralbelly (Dark Blue), Regal (Maroon), Prairie (Green), and Mississippi (Brown).

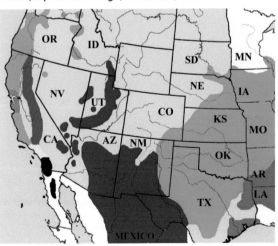

History: The Ring-necked Snake was first described by Spencer Fullerton Baird and Charles Frédéric Girard in 1853. The subsequent describers of subspecies are listed above after the scientific name of each subspecies.

Other Common Names: Arny's Ring-necked Snake, Red-bellied Snake, Punctated Viper Ring Snake, Ringneck Snake, and Western Ring-necked Snake.

Size: Small to medium. Ring-necked Snakes range from 8–34 in. (20.3–87 cm).

Identification: Smooth-scaled. The various subspecies have been separated from one another by scale counts, size, and other morphological characteristics, but all Ring-necked Snakes look very similar to one another. They are generally dark greenish gray or olive above, with an orange or yellow ring around the neck, but sometimes the Regal Ring-necked Snake often lacks the ring. The belly is yellow, orange, or red, with a double or triple row of small, half-moon shaped black spots extending from the neck to the tail. The underside of the tail is red, and when alarmed the snake will coil it into a corkscrew shape, displaying the red color underneath as a warning to any would-be predators. Occasionally very dark individuals will be found (melanistic), which do not have the neck ring or the orange belly. In some areas the neck ring can be three or four times longer than normal.

Brood Size: Egg-layers. A clutch of 2–10 eggs are generally laid in June or July. Sometimes a second clutch will be laid in the same season.

Range: From coast to coast, but the range is limited in the West. Apparently absent from most of Oregon (dry side), Washington, Idaho, Utah, Nevada, and South Dakota. Absent from all of Montana, North Dakota, Wyoming, western two-thirds of Nebraska, and extreme western Kansas.

Prey: Eats salamanders, small frogs, tadpoles, small snakes (including juvenile Mountain Kingsnakes), insects, slugs, lizards, and earthworms.

Habitat: Terrestrial. From sea-level to around 7,200 feet (2,200 m). Found in grassland, oak-woodland, pine forest, riparian zones, rocky hillsides, leaf litter, gardens, and chaparral. Active on the surface only when it is moist, or after dark.

Notes: This species may be venomous to some predators, including certain snakes.

Regal Ring-necked Snake (*Diadophis punctatus regalis*).

Photo: Alan St. John

Regal Ring-necked Snake
Venter (*D. p. regalis*)

Photo: Brian Hubbs

NW Ring-necked Snake (*D. p. occidentalis*). Photo: Alan St. John

Prairie Ring-necked Snake (*D. p. arnyi*). Photo: Matt Cage

Texas Indigo Snake (*Drymarchon melanurus erebennus*). Photo: Bill Love

Texas Indigo Snake
Drymarchon melanurus erebennus
Protected by law in TX

Species & Subspecies: The Texas Indigo Snake (*Drymarchon melanurus erebennus*) Cope, 1860, occurs in the U.S. There are other subspecies found south of the border.

History: The genus *Drymarchon* was first described by Leopold Fitzinger in 1843, while the species *Drymarchon melanurus* was described by André Duméril, Gabriel Bibron, and Auguste Duméril in 1854. One of two Indigo Snake species found within the United States, but the only one occurring in the west, the Texas Indigo Snake (*Drymarchon melanurus erebennus*) was described by Edward Cope in 1860.

Other Common Names: American Corais Snake, Black Snake, Blue Bull Snake, Blue Gopher Snake, Cribo, Gopher Snake, Indigo Snake, Mexican Black Snake, Mexican Gopher Snake, Mexican Indigo Snake, Mexican Rat Snake, and Tropical Indigo Snake.

Size: Very Large. Adult Texas Indigo Snakes are usually between 60–78 in. (152–198 cm), with a record size of 100¼ in. (255 cm).

Identification: Smooth-scaled. Bluish black, except for forepart of body

which may be brownish with slight pattern. Reddish chin and sides of head. There are downward dark lines from the eyes.

Brood Size: Egg-layers. Generally lays 10–12 eggs in the spring.

Range: Found roughly from the confluence of the Rio Grande and Pecos Rivers in west Texas to around Port Lavaca on the Gulf Coast, and south into Mexico, but apparently absent from immediate vicinity of San Antonio. There are reports of this snake following the Rio Grande as far west as Langtry.

Prey: Consumes almost anything it can catch and swallow, from small mammals to birds, frogs, lizards, and snakes (even venomous snakes).

Habitat: Terrestrial. Prefers fairly open or lightly vegetated areas not far from permanent water, such as creeks, ponds, lakes, canals, and rivers. Also inhabits grassland, mesquite savannah, and coastal sand dunes.

Notes: A fast and docile creature, but when threatened and cornered, this snake will flatten its neck, hiss loudly, vibrate its tail. However, it seldom attempts to bite. When I found my first and only Texas Indigo in Val Verde County, Texas I wasn't sure what I was looking at. The snake was rapidly exiting a stream bed and moving at considerable speed up and over the bank. I suspected it was an Indigo, and chased it a few yards for a positive identification. When I finally grabbed the snake, it hissed loudly, but settled down in a few minutes with gentle handling, never attempting to bite. These snakes are currently protected in Texas and considered a Threatened Species.

Texas Indigo Snake (*Drymarchon melanurus erebennus*). Photo: Troy Hibbitts

Western Mudsnake (*Farancia abacura reinwardtii*). Photo: Brian Hubbs

Western Mudsnake
Farancia abacura

Species & Subspecies: The Western Mudsnake (*Farancia abacura reinwardtii*) Schlegal, 1837.

History: The species *Farancia abacura* was first described by John Edwards Holbrook in 1836 as *Coluber abacurus*, and the subspecies *reinwardtii* was first described by Hermann Schlegel in 1837.

Other Common Names: Checkered Snake, Dart Snake, Hoop Snake, Horn Snake, Horn Tail, North American Red-bellied Snake, Red-bellied Horn Snake, Stingaree, Stinging Snake, Thunder Snake, and Wampum Snake.

Size: Large. Adults average 40–54 in. (102–137 cm), with the record being 81½ in. (207 cm).

Identification: Smooth-scaled. A shiny, black snake with 52 or fewer alternating red blotches on most of the lower 2 scale rows along the sides, and a red and black checkered belly. Tail has a hard spine on the tip (blunt in adults).

Brood Size: Egg-layer. From 4–104 (average 30–50) eggs are usually laid in June or July.

Range: Eastern and southeastern Texas, extreme southeastern Oklahoma to northeastern Arkansas, all of Louisiana, southeastern Missouri, southern Illinois and southwestern Indiana, western Kentucky and Tennessee, all of Mississippi, and western Alabama (Blue area on map). Eastern Alabama is an intergrade zone (Gray on map) between the Western and Eastern Mudsnakes.

Prey: Mud snakes eat eel-like salamanders called Amphiumas (favored prey), but Sirens, other amphibians, and fish are occasionally taken.

Habitat: Aquatic. This is a snake of the southern swamps, streams, and lowlands. It is equally at home underground in burrows or in water. It is never found far from water and its aquatic prey. Normally secretive and nocturnal in its habits, seldom moving about on the surface until at least dusk.

Notes: This is one of the mythological "Hoop" snakes, which are thought by some to grab their tail in their mouth and roll downhill. The tail spine is thought to be a stinger, because when held these snakes may press the tail against the collector's hand. It is not a stinger, and the snakes do not grab their tails in their mouths and roll downhill. Their habit of lying in a loose coil on the ground, and the human tendency to create as outlandish a story as possible, inspired the "Hoop" snake legend.

Juvenile Western Mudsnake (*Farancia abacura reinwardtii*) venter.
Photo: Bill Love

Western Hook-nosed Snake (*Gyalopian canum*). Photo: Brian Hubbs

Hook-nosed Snakes
Ficimia streckeri, Gyalopian canum, & Gyalopian quadrangulare

Genera & Species: There are two genera and three species of Hook-nosed Snakes that occur in the western U.S., the Western Hook-nosed Snake (*Gyalopian canum*), Thornscrub Hook-nosed Snake (*Gyalopian quadrangulare*), and the Mexican Hook-nosed Snake (*Ficimia streckeri*).

History: The Western Hook-nosed Snake (*Gyalopian canum*) was first described by Edward Cope in 1860, while the Thornscrub Hook-nosed Snake (*Gyalopian quadrangulare*) was described by Albert Günther in 1893, and the Mexican Hook-nosed Snake (*Ficimia streckeri*) was described by Edward Taylor in 1931.

Other Common Names: Dog-nose Snake, Dog-nosed Snake, Pug-nosed Snake, Strecker's Hook-nosed Snake, and South Texas Hook-nosed Snake.

Size: Small. From 6–15 in. (15–38 cm), depending on species.

Identification: All three Hook-nosed Snakes are smooth-scaled, with an upturned snout. The Western Hook-nosed Snake (*Gyalopian canum*) is grayish, yellowish-gray, or tan with 25–48 or more brown blotches or bands on the body. The Thornscrub Hook-nosed Snake (*Gyalopian quadrangulare*) is a strikingly colored serpent with black bands, white to cream interspaces along top of back, and a reddish stripe (broken by the black bands) along

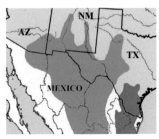

Hook-nosed Snake
Range Maps

Left: Western Hook-nosed Snake (Green) and Mexican Hook-nosed Snake (Blue).

Right: Thornscrub Hook-nosed Snake

each side. The Mexican Hook-nosed Snake (*Ficimia streckeri*) is pale or medium gray, greenish gray, or brownish gray, with 33–60 dark olive to black thin crossbands or spots down the back. The bands can be broken in places.

Brood Size: Egg-layer. Reproduction is poorly known for these snakes, but the Western Hook-nosed and Mexican Hook-nosed Snakes are known to lay up to 5 eggs, while the Thornscrub Hook-nosed Snake is known to lay up to 6 eggs.

Range: The Western Hook-nosed Snake is found from southeastern Arizona through southern New Mexico (and Rio Grande and Pecos Valleys) to western Texas, and south into Mexico. The Thornscrub Hook-nosed Snake is found from extreme southern Arizona (Pajarito and Patagonia Mountains area) south into Mexico. The Mexican Hook-nosed Snake is found from south Texas into eastern Mexico.

Prey: Hook-nosed Snakes feed on spiders, centipedes, scorpions, and other insects. Captive individuals have also fed on lizards, small snakes, and mice.

Habitat: Terrestrial. The Western Hook-nosed Snake is found from 1,000–6,890 feet (330–2,100 m), Thornscrub Hook-nosed Snake is found from near sea-level to 4,400 feet (1,340 m), and the Mexican Hook-nosed Snake is found from near sea-level to 4,900 feet (1,494 m) at the southern edge of its range in Mexico. Extremely fossorial, spending most of their lives underground in sandy desert and scrub habitats, but also extend into foothills and rocky and gravelly conditions.

Notes: When touched or threatened in the wild, the Western Hook-nosed Snake will writhe and contort its body (similar to the Hog-nosed Snakes) and evert the lining of the vent, while making a popping or bubbling sound.

Mexican Hook-nosed Snake
(*Ficimia streckeri*)

Photo: Troy Hibbitts

Thornscrub Hook-nosed Snake
(*Gyalopian quadrangulare*)

Photo: Bill Love

Plains Hog-nosed Snake (*Heterodon nasicus*). Photo: Brian Hubbs

Hog-nosed Snakes

Heterodon gloydi, Heterodon kennerlyi, Heterodon nasicus, &
Heterodon platirhinos
Protected by law in KS

Species: Four species are found within the scope of this book, Dusty Hog-nosed Snake (*Heterodon gloydi*) Edgren, 1952; Mexican Hog-nosed Snake (*Heterodon kennerlyi*) Kennicott, 1860; Plains Hog-nosed Snake (*Heterodon nasicus*) Baird and Girard, 1852; and Eastern Hog-nosed Snake (*Heterodon platirhinos*) Latreille, 1801.

History: The North American Hog-nosed Snake (*Heterodon*) was first described by Pierre Andre Latreille in 1801.

Other Common Names: Bastard Rattlesnake, Black Adder, Black Blowing Viper, Black Viper Snake, Blow Snake, Blower, Blowing Viper, Bluffer, Buckwheat-nose Snake, Calico Snake, Checkered Adder, Chunk Head, Deaf Adder, Faux Viper, Flat-headed Adder, Hay-nose Snake, Hissing Adder, Hissing Viper, Hognose Snake, Play-Possum Snake, Poison Viper, Prairie Hog-nosed Snake, Puff Adder, Puffing Adder, Red Snake, Rock Adder, Rossel Bastard, Sand Adder, Sand Snake, Spoonbill Snake, Spotted Adder, Spreadhead Snake, Spread-head viper, Spreading Adder, Texas Hog-nosed Snake, Texas Rooter, and Western Hog-nosed Snake.

Hog-nosed Snake
Range Maps

Left: Plains Hog-nosed Snake (Blue), Mexican Hog-nosed Snake (Red), & Dusty Hog-nosed Snake (Green). Intergrade zone in Gray.

Right: Eastern Hog-nosed Snake.

44

Size: Small to medium. Adult Dusty, Plains, and Mexican Hog-nosed Snakes are 15–36 in. (38–92 cm). Adult Eastern Hog-nosed Snakes are 20–33 in. (51–84 cm), with a record size of 45½ in. (115.6 cm).

Identification: Keeled scales. Snout upturned. Western species are light tan to light brown with 35–40 darker blotches along the back and smaller spots on each side. The belly is mostly dark. Eastern Hog-nosed Snakes are variable in color, and can be yellow, brown, gray, black, olive, orange, or reddish, with 20–30 darker blotches as in western species, but generally the blotches are larger. Occasionally all black or all gray. Belly can be solid yellowish, pinkish or gray, or mottled with gray or greenish. Underside of tail may be lighter than the belly.

Brood Size: Egg-layer. The western species lay from 4–25 eggs, while the Eastern Hog-nosed Snake lays 8–40.

Range: Western species (Dusty, Plains, and Mexican) are found from southeast Arizona through the eastern two-thirds of New Mexico and western Texas (and south into Mexico) northward through the western Plains states to western Montana and extreme southern Canada. Isolated populations in northwestern New Mexico, eastern Texas, and central Wyoming. Other isolated populations in Missouri, Iowa, Illinois, Minnesota, and southwest Tennessee.
Eastern Hog-nosed Snake is found from the eastern two-thirds of Texas, north to southern South Dakota, and east through the Atlantic states.

Prey: The western species primarily eat toads, but have been known to also take frogs, lizards, mice, snakes, salamanders, turtles, and bird and reptile eggs. The Eastern Hog-nosed Snake is primarily a toad eater, but will also take frogs.

Habitat: Terrestrial. The western species prefer sandy areas within grasslands, sand hills, dry river bottoms, and Chihuahuan desert. Eastern Hog-nosed Snakes prefer sandy areas in almost any type of habitat.

Notes: Despite the proliferation of regional common names containing the word Adder and Viper, this snake is harmless to humans and seldom actually bites anything but its prey. Most of its predator avoidance act revolves around a series of bluffs. First, the snake will spread its neck into a hood shape and act very menacing. This is often followed by hisses and strikes at the offending object, but these seldom actually connect as the mouth is usually closed. If these two actions fail to drive away the intruder, and the snake is still alive, then the real act begins. It starts to wiggle around, roll from side to side, and generally acts wounded. These convulsions are followed by the snake flipping onto its back, spreading fecal matter all over itself, opening its mouth, and extending the tongue. For all intents and purposes, it now appears to be dead, but if flipped right-side-up it will immediately return to the dead position. Evidently, to its thinking, a dead snake should be upside down at all times. If the snake survives to go through all of these scenarios the observer will have witnessed one of nature's most comical acts, and if left alone, the Hog-nosed Snake will "wake up" in a few minutes, turn its head, survey the surroundings, and if all clear, crawl away to safety. Unfortunately, many Hog-nosed Snakes never make it past Act 1 when encountered by ignorant humans, and "dead" becomes Act 2 for real.

Eastern Hog-nosed Snake (*Heterodon platirhinos*). Photo: Matt Cage

 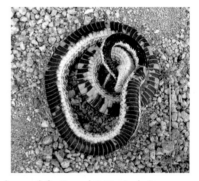

Mexican Hog-nosed Snake (*Heterodon kennerlyi*). Dorsal & Ventral views.
Photos: Brian Hubbs

Eastern Hog-nosed Snake (*Heterodon platirhinos*) Venter. Photo: Matt Cage

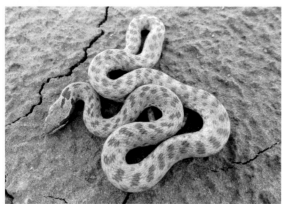

Northern Desert Night Snake (*Hypsiglena chlorophaea deserticola*).
Photo: Brian Hubbs

Nightsnakes
Hypsiglena chlorophaea, Hypsiglena jani, & Hypsiglena ochrorhyncha
Chihuahuan Nightsnake (*Hypsiglena jani*) Protected by law in KS
Mildly Venomous

Species & Subspecies: There are three species of Nightsnakes currently recognized in the western U.S., and six subspecies.

1) Desert Nightsnake (*Hypsiglena chlorophaea*) Cope, 1860:
    Northern Desert Nightsnake (*Hypsiglena chlorophaea deserticola*) Tanner, 1944
    Mesa Verde Nightsnake (*Hypsiglena chlorophaea loreala*) Tanner, 1944
    Sonoran Nightsnake (*Hypsiglena chlorophaea chlorophaea*) Cope, 1860.
2) Chihuahuan Nightsnake (*Hypsiglena jani*) Duges, 1866:
    Texas Nightsnake (*Hypsiglena jani texana*) Stejneger, 1893
3) Coast Nightsnake (*Hypsiglena ochrorhyncha*) Cope, 1860:
    California Nightsnake (*Hypsiglena ochrorhyncha nuchalata*) Tanner, 1943
    San Diego Nightsnake (*Hypsiglena ochrorhyncha klauberi*) Tanner, 1944.

History: The genus *Hypsiglena* was first described by Edward Cope in 1860. Many publications still use the old name *Hypsiglena torquata* for all U.S. Night Snake species and subspecies, and the three species named here have been recently carved out of that old name (Mulcahy, 2008) based on DNA analysis. While these are the currently accepted names, there is still some debate over whether they are valid. To compound matters, most Night Snakes in the U.S. tend to be indistinguishable from one another at a cursory glance.

Other Common Names: Spotted Nightsnake, Texan Rock Snake, and Xantus' Snake.
Size: Small. Adults are normally 12–26 in. (30-66 cm).
Identification: Smooth-scaled. Vertical, cat-like pupils. This is a light brown, tan, or grayish snake

with 50–70 irregular darker spots or blotches of brown down the mid-back, and a lower set of smaller spots along the sides. Sometimes the spots are smaller and broken into pairs or trios. There is a darker stripe on each side of the head that begins at the snout and runs through the eye to the rear of the head. The top of the rear portion of the head can have a dark elongate marking, often pointed in shape. The belly is yellowish or white. Most Night Snakes look very similar to one another, even the different species, but will vary in ground color shades and amount of spotting.

Brood Size: Egg-layer. A clutch of 2–9 eggs are laid from April to September, depending on latitude and elevation.

Range: Found from coastal California, central Oregon and Washington, southeastward through southern Idaho, most of Utah and New Mexico, southeastern Colorado, southern Kansas, and western Oklahoma to the western two-thirds of Texas, and south into mainland Mexico and most of Baja California. Isolated population in eastern Texas.

Prey: Small lizards (especially Side-blotched Lizards) and their eggs, small snakes, salamanders, toads, frogs, insects, and possibly scorpions.

Habitat: Terrestrial. From sea-level to 8,700 feet (2,650 m). These small snakes are at home from the deserts to the high mountains, occurring in sand, clay, loam, or rocky soil; chaparral, grassland, oak woodland, sagebrush, meadows, thornscrub, and pine forests.

Notes: Injects mild venom into prey through enlarged grooved teeth at rear of upper jaw. Seldom tries to bite, and is not considered harmful to humans. This is one of the more abundant small snakes. It is primarily nocturnal, so it is seldom encountered unless on roadways at night or under surface debris. In certain areas it is the most common serpent, and overall plentiful throughout its range. Many consider this to be a desert species, but I have seen large concentrations of these snakes high in the Sierra Nevada Mountains above 6,000 feet (1,829 m).

The range map does not show boundaries for the different species or subspecies as most have been recently resurrected, and some disagreement exists as to whether all are even valid.

San Diego Night Snake
(*Hypsiglena ochrorhyncha klauberi*)

Photo: Brian Hubbs

Gray-banded Kingsnake (*Lampropeltis alterna*) Blair's morph
Photo: Brian Hubbs

Gray-banded Kingsnake
Lampropeltis alterna
Protected by law in NM

Species: Gray-banded Kingsnake (*Lampropeltis alterna*).

History: The Gray-banded Kingsnake was first described as *Ophibolus alternus* by Arthur Erwin Brown in 1901. Later, the name was changed to *Lampropeltis alterna* by Leonhard Stejneger & Thomas Barbour in 1917. Still later, the now defunct subspecies *Lampropeltis alterna blairi* was described by Alvin Flury in 1950, based on the saddled phase of this snake. It was named in honor of William Franklin Blair, a Texas biologist. It is now known that both the *alterna* and *blairi* pattern phases (see Identification) can be produced from the same clutch of eggs, so the *blairi* subspecies was dropped in 1970 by Ernest C. Tanzer, however, the saddled phase is still referred to as a Blair's morph.

Other Common Names: Alterna, Blair's, Blair's Kingsnake, Davis Mountain Kingsnake, and Davis Mountains Kingsnake.

Size: Medium to large. Adults are 20–57 in. (51–145 cm).

Identification: Smooth-scaled. This kingsnake is interesting because of its diversity of colors and patterns in the wild. It is found in two basic patterns, the Alterna morph and the Blair's morph. Both morphs can have a background color of light, medium, or dark gray, but the Alterna morph has 17–33 black bands, bars, or wedges (often split by orange or red coloration) outlined by white along the back. Between many of the the black bands are thinner, broken crossbands of small black dots that are usually in groups of three to five (called alternates). Some Alterna morphs are very colorful, having bright orange wedges surrounded by black, while others will lack the orange color altogether. The Blair's morph almost looks like a completely different species by comparison. While it is found in the same shades of gray, its pattern

generally consists of 12–15 wide orange or reddish saddles, outlined in black, which is also outlined by white. There is also a longish nuchal blotch which begins on the neck and is roughly twice as long as any of the saddles. The "alternates" are usually missing on this morph, but can be found on a small percentage, depending on which genes were inherited from the parents. Gray-banded Kingsnakes from the eastern portion of the range favor the Blair's morph, while those found farther west are almost always Alterna morphs, yet both patterns can be found in almost any brood. In addition to these two basic morphs, another pattern is found in the Davis Mountains region, and consists of basically black speckles on a medium gray or brown background.

Brood Size: Egg-layer. Lays 3–13 eggs in summer.

Range: Found primarily in the Trans-Pecos and western Edwards Plateau regions in Texas, north into extreme southeast New Mexico (vicinity of Carlsbad Caverns and Guadalupe Mountains), and south into Mexico.

Prey: Favored food is lizards, but will also eat small rodents and probably other snakes.

Habitat: Terrestrial. This is a snake of the semi-arid Chihuahuan Desert region and higher mountain elevations within that area. It is typically found in areas of limestone or other rocky substrate. It prefers hilly terrain, but is also present in river valleys. A secretive serpent by nature, the Gray-banded Kingsnake is seldom seen during daylight hours, preferring to move about after dark.

Notes: Constrictors. These attractive snakes have been the holy grail of many snake collectors for over 50 years. Until the early 1970s little was known about their habits or area of occupation. What is known today is due to over 40 years of road-collecting by Gray-banded Kingsnake enthusiasts. Hundreds of these people have participated in summer searches all over west Texas, discovering the proper times and situations to see these snakes, and at the same time adding valuable natural history and range information to science. The vast majority of snakes were discovered crossing roads, or on the edge of roads, after dark. If this snake had not become so popular with snake breeders and kingsnake seekers we would probably still know next to nothing about its distribution, habits, and abundance. Fortunately, due to their efforts we now know that this is a common, yet extremely secretive serpent that occupies a large range in a relatively unpopulated part of the U.S. It is popular in the pet trade, and thousands have been produced in captivity from wild stock collected in Texas. However, despite all this attention, perhaps 99% of its range has never been explored, as it lies within thousands of square miles of road-less terrain or on vast private ranches.

Gray-banded Kingsnake
(*Lampropeltis alterna*)
Alterna morph

Photo: Troy Hibbitts

Prairie Kingsnake (*Lampropeltis calligaster*) from Kansas.
Photo: Brian Hubbs

Prairie Kingsnake
(Yellow-bellied Kingsnake)
Lampropeltis calligaster

Species & Subspecies: The Yellow-bellied Kingsnake (*Lampropeltis calligaster*) has three subspecies, one of which occurs in the western U.S.: the Prairie Kingsnake (*Lampropeltis calligaster calligaster*).

History: The Prairie Kingsnake (*Lampropeltis calligaster calligaster*) was first described by Richard Harlan in 1827 as *Coluber calligaster*, which was later changed to *Lampropeltis calligaster* by Edward Cope in 1860.

Other Common Names: Blotched Kingsnake, Brown Kingsnake, Kansas Kingsnake, and Yellow-bellied Kingsnake.

Size: Medium. Adults average 30–42 in. (76–107 cm), with a record size of 56 in. (142.7 cm).

Identification: Smooth-scaled. This is usually a brown on brown blotched kingsnake. Its pattern consists of a series of 40–78 dark brown blotches (often split into pairs) on a lighter shade of brown. Occasionally the blotches are fused together forming a lengthwise stripe down the center of the back. Older individuals and snakes from certain regions will be very faded and appear to have no pattern at all. The belly is yellowish or cream, with small dark spots or blotches.

Brood Size: Egg-layer. Lays 5–15 eggs, usually in June or July.

Range: Found from southeastern Nebraska, southwestward through Kansas and Oklahoma, south in the eastern half of Texas to the Gulf of Mexico around Corpus Christie, and eastward through southern Iowa, all of Missouri and Arkansas, western Louisiana, southern Illinois, western Kentucky, and northwestern Tennessee.

Prey: Like other kingsnakes, this one is known to consume small rodents, birds, lizards, frogs, and other snakes.

Habitat: Terrestrial. As the name suggests, these snakes are primarily found in prairie habitats, but are also

51

common in wooded edge, river plains, and valley bottoms.

Notes: Constrictors. Pattern is very similar to the Great Plains Rat Snake, which overlaps with this kingsnake over most of its range, but has a divided anal plate and faintly keeled scales. The Prairie Kingsnake has a solid (single) anal plate.

Two color pattern variations of Prairie Kingsnakes from Kentucky
Photos: Phil Peak

Common Kingsnake - California Kingsnake (*Lampropeltis getula californiae*)
Black & White Banded morph.   Photo: Brian Hubbs

Common Kingsnake
Lampropeltis getula
Speckled Kingsnake (*L. g. holbrooki*) is Protected by law in CO & NE
California Kingsnake (*L. g. californiae*) Protected by law in OR & UT

Species & Subspecies: There is one species and eight subspecies of Common Kingsnakes that occur within the United States, four of which are found in the western half of the country:

California Kingsnake (*Lampropeltis getula californiae*) Blainville, 1835
Western Black Kingsnake (*Lampropeltis getula nigrita*) Zweifel & Norris, 1955
Desert Kingsnake (*Lampropeltis getula splendida*) Baird & Girard, 1853
Speckled Kingsnake (*Lampropeltis getula holbrooki*) Stejneger, 1902.

History: The Common Kingsnake (*Lampropeltis getula*) was first described in 1766 as *Coluber getulus* by Carolus Linnaeus, a Swedish zoologist who is considered the father of modern taxonomy.

Common Kingsnake
Range Map

California Kingsnake (Blue)
W. Black Kingsnake (Black)
Desert Kingsnake (Red)
Speckled Kingsnake (Green)
Intergrade zones (Gray)

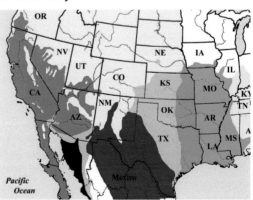

Other Common Names: Banded Kingsnake, Blaineville's Kingsnake, Striped Kingsnake, Fresno King Snake, Boyle's Kingsnake, and Yuma Kingsnake (for California Kingsnakes); Mexican Black Kingsnake (for the Western Black Kingsnake); Sonoran Kingsnake, Splendid Kingsnake, Boundary Kingsnake, and Mexican Kingsnake (for Desert Kingsnakes); and Say's Kingsnake, Chicken Snake, Holbrook's Kingsnake, Salt & Pepper Snake, Speckled Adder, Southern Kingsnake, Spotted Kingsnake, Yellow-spotted Kingsnake, and Yellow-spotted Black Snake (for the Speckled Kingsnake).

Size: Large. Adults range from 24–78 in. (61–198 cm).

Identification: Smooth-scaled. The *California Kingsnake* is found in many patterns and colors (morphs). Typically, it is a black and white or brown and yellow banded serpent with 21–48 dark bands across the body from the head to the beginning of the tail. These two morphs are the ones most people are familiar with. Desert regions favor the black and white coloration, while elsewhere brown and yellow predominates. However, there are over 70 other natural color/pattern combinations for this variable snake, depending upon which portion of the range you happen to be in. These include the speckled banded morph, dotted morph, striped morphs, blotched morphs, barred morphs, mud morphs, unicolor morphs, albino morphs, hypo-melanistic morphs, hyper-melanistic morphs, and lavender morphs. The areas in California that were historically wet and marshy produce the striped patterns and aberrant morphs (atypical patterns), namely San Diego and Riverside counties, Los Angeles and Orange counties, and the San Joaquin Valley and Delta regions. Those areas contain four different striped patterns and a host of aberrant morphs. The San Diego Striped Pattern consists of a lengthwise light stripe, either full or broken on a dark body. Striping or dots are found on top of the tail, and various amounts of light speckling can be present on the sides of the snake. In Los Angeles and Orange counties we find the Newport-Long Beach Striped Pattern, which is similar to the San Diego Pattern, except that the top of the tail is always dark and there are side blotches instead of speckles. The San Joaquin Valley is home to the Eiseni Striped Pattern, which always starts out banded, but ends striped. No two look identical, and the pattern can involve light yellow blotches, squiggles, bands, stripes, and dots on a dark brown background. However, the belly is always mostly or solid black or grayish black. There is even a fully banded, black-bellied version found in the same area. Farther north in the Delta region, the Eiseni Pattern changes to the Delta Pattern, which consists of the same morphs as the Eiseni group, but is a lighter shade of brown and the yellow color is replaced by tan, light brown, pewter, or rust. The belly is also mostly or solid brown. There are seven photos of California Kingsnake morphs and patterns in this book for general reference. For detailed information on all 74 California Kingsnake morphs, their ranges, habits, and habitats, see my book "Common Kingsnakes," also from Tricolor Books, which contains 115 pages devoted to this subspecies.

The *Desert Kingsnake* is usually dark brown to blackish, with a series of 42–97 square, rectangular, or cross-banded dark areas created by yellow or white speckled bars along the back. The sides are usually speckled with white or yellow to some degree. The head is dark. The belly ranges from mottled with dark pigment to almost solid dark. The young are exactly like the adults in pattern and color.

The *Western Black Kingsnake* is either solid black or has a faint Desert Kingsnake-type pattern. The belly is usually solid black or dark brown. The young can be either solid black or brightly marked like a Desert Kingsnake, which turns completely or mostly dark with age.

The *Speckled Kingsnake* is black, greenish, or greenish-black, with numerous yellow, orange, or white speckles all over the body. In some areas there are thin bars of the lighter color spaced evenly down the back, surrounded by speckles. The belly is light, with varying amounts of dark bars or blotches. The head is dark, with a varying amount of light speckles and small bars. The young are solidly dark with heavy bars of light color down the back.

Brood Size: Egg-layers. Clutch sizes range from 2–24 eggs (average 6–12), laid from May to August, with hatching taking place from late July to October.

Range: Nationwide, but absent from most areas north of the 40th Parallel (See Range map).

Prey: The primary diet of Common Kingsnakes consists of rodents, lizards (including the venomous Gila Monster), and smaller snakes (including venomous species and other kingsnakes), but birds and their eggs, small turtles, and also some amphibians (frogs) are also known to be taken occasionally.

Habitat: Terrestrial. From sea-level to over 7,000 feet (2,134 m) in the eastern Sierra Nevada Mountains. These snakes are habitat generalists, being found in almost every habitat within their elevational and geographic ranges, except for flat, un-vegetated desert.

Notes: Constrictors. These snakes are common to abundant where they occur. My conservative estimate for just the California population of California Kingsnakes is over 120 million statewide. I have personally found over 2,600 in the wild during the last 20 years, and one isolated, walled, six-acre site in Los Angeles County has yielded over 50 different California Kingsnakes in the last three years. Each was photographed, and band counts were used to verify new snakes and repeat sightings. To date, only about 15% of the property has been sampled, so the future numbers have nowhere to go but up.

Desert Kingsnake
(*Lampropeltis getula splendida*)

Photo: Joe Forks

Speckled Kingsnake
(*Lampropeltis getula
holbrooki*) from near
Houston, TX

Photo: Clint Pustejovsky

W. Black Kingsnake
(*Lampropeltis getula
nigrita*).

Photo: Bill Love

Intergrade
California x Desert Kingsnake
from southeastern Arizona.

Photo: Brian Hubbs

A Few California Kingsnake Morphs

Above Left: Newport-Long Beach Pattern.   Above Right: San Diego Striped Pattern
Photos: Brian Hubbs

Above Left: Barred Morph.   Above Right: Eiseni Striped Pattern
Photos: Brian Hubbs

Above Left: Golden Brown Banded Morph.   Above Right: Speckled Banded Morph
Photos: Brian Hubbs

San Diego Mountain Kingsnake (*Lampropeltis zonata pulchra*)
Photo: Brian Hubbs

Mountain Kingsnakes

Lampropeltis pyromelana & Lampropeltis zonata
San Diego Mountain Kingsnake (*L. z. pulchra*) is Protected by law in CA
Saint Helena Mountain Kingsnake (*L. z. zonata*) is Protected by law in OR & WA
Utah Mountain Kingsnake [(*L. p. infralabialis*) is Protected by law in NV & UT

Species & Subspecies: There are two species of Mountain Kingsnakes in the western U.S., the California Mountain Kingsnake (*Lampropeltis zonata*) and the Sonoran Mountain Kingsnake (*Lampropeltis pyromelana*). Each has subspecies within the western U.S. The Sonoran Mountain Kingsnake has two and the California Mountain Kingsnake has five.

The subspecies belonging to the Sonoran Mountain Kingsnake (*Lampropeltis pyromelana*) include: Utah Mountain Kingsnake (*Lampropeltis pyromelana infralabialis*) Tanner, 1953 and the Arizona Mountain Kingsnake (*Lampropeltis pyromelana pyromelana*) Cope, 1867.

California Mountain Kingsnake (*Lampropeltis zonata*) subspecies include:

Mountain Kingsnake
Range Maps

Left: Northern CA Mtn Kingsnake (Blue), Coast Mtn Kingsnake (Brown), San Bernardino Mtn Kingsnake (Lavender), San Diego Mtn Kingsnake (Red) & Intergrade zones (Yellow).

Right: Utah Mtn Kingsnake (Blue) & Arizona Mtn Kingsnake (Red).

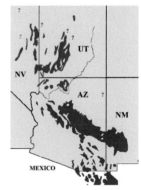

Saint Helena Mountain Kingsnake (*Lampropeltis zonata zonata*) Lockington, 1876; Sierra Mountain Kingsnake (*Lampropeltis zonata multicincta*) Yarrow, 1882; Coast Mountain Kingsnake (*Lampropeltis zonata multifasciata*) Bocourt, 1886; San Bernardino Mountain Kingsnake (*Lampropeltis zonata parvirubra*) Zweifel, 1952; and San Diego Mountain Kingsnake (*Lampropeltis zonata pulchra*) Zweifel, 1952.

History: The California Mountain Kingsnake (*Lampropeltis zonata*) was described by W. N. Lockington in 1876, long after an incomplete description by M. H. De Blainville in 1835. The Sonoran Mountain Kingsnake (*Lampropeltis pyromelana*) was described by Edward Cope in 1867.

Other Common Names: Arizona Kingsnake, Arizona Milk Snake, Arizona Ringed Snake, Coral Kingsnake, Coral Snake, Coral Milk Snake, Corral Snake, Mountain Coral Snake, Ringed Kingsnake, Sierra Coral Snake, and Western Coral Kingsnake.

Size: Medium to large. Adult California Mountain Kingsnakes range from 20–47 in. (51–119.4 cm) in length, while adult Sonoran Mountain Kingsnakes average 24–40 in. (61–102 cm), with a record size of 62 in. (157.5 cm).

Identification: Smooth-scaled. One of the supposed "Coral Snake mimics" due to the similarity in colors, but the arrangement is different. These are the "Red touch Black, my friend Jack" snakes. The California Mountain Kingsnake is a very attractive and distinctive looking serpent that is often confused with the venomous Coral Snake, which does not occur anywhere within this snake's range. It has a black snout and red rings bordered by black rings, which are bordered by white or cream rings. In some individuals, most or all of the red rings may be lacking or incomplete (appearing as red wedges on the lower sides), especially in the Merced River drainage within and around Yosemite National Park, most of the range in extreme northern California and the states of Oregon and Washington, and scattered localities throughout the rest of the range. San Diego subspecies generally has 37 or fewer white body rings (excluding tail), the San Bernardino subspecies has 37 or more white body rings, the Coast subspecies generally has red on the head, and the Northern subspecies has wider white rings than the other three subspecies. There is an area of intergradation between the San Diego and San Bernardino subspecies in Riverside County (portions of the San Jacinto and Santa Rosa Mountains), where snakes may resemble either subspecies.

The Sonoran Mountain Kingsnake is a colorful serpent like the California Mountain Kingsnake, but has a white, off-white, or yellowish snout. The ranges of the two species do not overlap.

Brood Size: Egg-layers. California Mountain Kingsnakes lay from 1–10 or more eggs, with an average of 3–5. Sonoran Mountain Kingsnakes will usually lay 3–9 eggs, but have been known to lay as many as 15 in captivity.

Range: The California Mountain Kingsnake is found in almost all non-desert mountain ranges from San Diego County, California to southern Washington. It can be found in coastal and peninsular mountains as well as in the Sierra Nevada and Cascade Ranges. There are unverified reports and collections of this snake north of the known range in Oregon and around the known range in Washington, as well as in the White Mountains of eastern California (shown on map in light blue with question marks). It has also been reported by local residents on Santa Catalina Island, within the central Diablo Range, and in the La Panza Range, all in California (shown on map with question marks). The Sonoran Mountain Kingsnake ranges from the mountains of central Utah and eastern Nevada south through northwestern, central, and southeastern Arizona and southwestern New Mexico into northern Mexico.

Prey: Both species primarily eat lizards and small rodents, but will also consume small birds, their eggs, and other snakes (including rattlesnakes).

Habitat: Terrestrial. The California Mountain Kingsnake is found from sea level to over 9,000 feet (2743 m). It occurs in canyons, on chaparral covered hillsides, in oak woodland, pine-oak forest, and riparian areas. Elevation varies with location, but roughly begins at sea level on the central coast, 3,000 feet (914 m) in the mid-Sierra Nevada, and at 4,500 feet (1371 m) in San Diego County. Very secretive, it is seldom seen above ground unless conditions are moist or humid. Active after dark on warm evenings.

The Sonoran Mountain Kingsnake is found from 2,000–9,100 feet (610–2,775 m) the same types of habitat frequented by the California Mountain Kingsnake, but also follows riparian corridors very low into saguaro desert in a few places in Arizona. It is primarily diurnal (daylight active), but can also be active on warm nights. Generally secretive, but many have been found under the right conditions as they cross trails and roads, or wander along stream courses.

Notes: Constrictors. Considered "rare" by many misinformed naturalists, but these are actually a secretive and abundant resident within their preferred habitats. Estimates of abundance for the California species include 10–20 individuals per acre in good habitat, or a total population in California of over 30 million Mountain Kingsnakes.

Recent DNA research has currently eliminated the five California subspecies, but many disagree with this change, myself included. Based on morphological characteristics there should actually be four subspecies. On the Range Map I have shown four ranges, having combined the Saint Helena and Sierra subspecies, which together I now call the Northern California Mountain Kingsnake (area shaded in dark blue). All other ranges are depicted as in the past, as I feel they are still valid based on pattern characteristics alone. For additional, detailed information on all aspects of these snakes, their habits, ranges, and habitats, see my book, *"Mountain Kings,"* also by Tricolor Books.

Arizona Mtn Kingsnakes (*L. p. pyromelana*)
Photos: Brian Hubbs

California Mtn Kingsnakes (*L. zonata*). Top Left: Coast Mtn Kingsnake, Top Right: Sierra Mtn Kingsnake, Center: Sierra Mtn Kingsnake (dark), Bottom: San Bernardino Mtn Kingsnake.   Photos: Brian Hubbs

Pale Milk Snake (*Lampropeltis triangulum multistriata*)
Photo: Brian Hubbs

Milk Snake

Lampropeltis triangulum
Protected by law in Cochise County, AZ; and in CO, UT, and WY

Species & Subspecies: One species of Milk Snake (*Lampropeltis triangulum*) occurs within the western U.S, and there are seven subspecies: the Louisiana Milk Snake (*Lampropeltis triangulum amaura*) Cope, 1860; Mexican Milk Snake (*Lampropeltis triangulum annulata*) Kennicott, 1860; New Mexico Milk Snake (*Lampropeltis triangulum celaenops*) Stejneger, 1903; Central Plains Milk Snake (*Lampropeltis triangulum gentilis*) Baird and Girard, 1853; Pale Milk Snake (*Lampropeltis triangulum multistriata*) Kennicott, 1860; Red Milk Snake *(Lampropeltis triangulum syspila)* Cope, 1888; and Utah Milk Snake (*Lampropeltis triangulum taylori*) Tanner and Loomis, 1957.

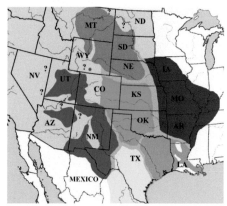

Milk Snake Range

New Mexico Milk Snake (Dark Blue)
Mexican Milk Snake (Yellow)
Louisiana Milk Snake (Light Blue)
Central Plains Milk Snake (Green)
Red Milk Snake (Maroon)
Pale Milk Snake (Orange)
Intergrade zones (Gray)

Note: The Utah Milk Snake range has been combined on this map with that of the New Mexico Milk Snake (See Notes section in text).

History: *Lampropeltis triangulum* was first described by Bernard Lacepede in 1789. It received its common name from early colonists who found Milk Snakes around their barns, and assumed the snakes were there to drink milk from the cows. As absurd as it sounds, this is the true origin of the name.

Other Common Names: Calico Snake, Chicken Snake, Coral King Snake, House Snake, Prairie Painted King Snake, Red King Snake, Ring Snake, Ringed Milk Snake, Saddled King Snake, Sand Coral, Scarlet Snake, Thunder Snake, Western King Snake, and Western Milk Snake.

Size: Small to medium. Adult western Milk Snakes are 16–43 in. (40.6–109 cm) in length, but the Eastern Milk Snake (not covered by this book) has been known to exceed 5 feet (1.5 m).

Identification: Smooth-scaled. These snakes are generally saddled or blotched with red or orange on a ground color of white, yellow, or gray. The saddles are bordered by a black outline. Generally the lower sides of the snake will be peppered with black or gray flecks within the ground color, but some individuals and subspecies do not follow this rule. The snout can be mostly black, gray, white, yellow, or mottled, depending again on the subspecies. The belly varies with subspecies, but usually has dark markings (bars or ovals) on white. Sometimes a portion of the red saddle will encroach onto the edge of the belly.

Brood Size: Egg-layer. From 1–20 eggs are laid from February to July, depending on region, climate, altitude, and subspecies.

Range: These snakes occur almost nationwide. They are found from Arizona, Utah, eastern Wyoming and Montana to the East Coast. The only states without a known Milk Snake population are California, Oregon, Washington, Idaho, North Dakota, and Florida. North Dakota probably has Milk Snakes that just haven't been discovered yet. The Scarlet Kingsnake replaces the Milk Snake in Florida, and was once thought to be a Milk Snake but isn't any longer.

Prey: Generally, Milk Snakes prey upon rodents and lizards, but also seek out young birds, bird eggs, reptile eggs, small snakes and invertebrates—including slugs, beetles and insects, and will even occasionally prey on young bats and fish.

Habitat: Terrestrial. Milk snakes are found from sea level in Texas to over 8,000 feet (2,438 m) in Colorado. Extremely subterranean, these snakes spend the majority of their lives underground, searching for prey in rodent burrows and rock crevices. They are found in grassland, chaparral, river and stream valleys, open woods, wooded edge, semi-desert, sand hills, edges of marshes, and on hillsides and mountain slopes, depending on the region.

Notes: Constrictors. This is another member of the kingsnake family. A more appropriate name might be "Saddled Kingsnake," but the current common name has been around so long it is doubtful it will ever be changed. Milk Snakes are often confused with Mountain Kingsnakes, but there are very few places where a person could encounter both, as they live in different habitats. The best rule to tell them apart is to look at the lower end of the pale bands. The Milk Snake has light bands that widen at the bottom. The bands do not widen on the Sonoran Mountain Kingsnake. Due to the coloration, these snakes could possibly be confused with the venomous Coral Snake, but the similarity is almost non-existent.

At this time there appears to be little morphological difference between the New Mexico and Utah subspecies, and these will be found combined on the range map.

Central Plains Milk Snake (*Lampropeltis triangulum gentilis*)
Photo: Brian Hubbs

Red Milk Snake (*Lampropeltis triangulum syspila*) above & New Mexico Milk Snake (*Lampropeltis triangulum celaenops*) below.
Photos: Brian Hubbs

Mexican Milk Snake (*Lampropeltis triangulum annulata*)
Photo: Troy Hibbitts

Louisiana Milk Snake (*Lampropeltis triangulum amaura*)
above, and a Texas barrier island Intergrade below.
Photos: Brian Hubbs

Northern Cat-eyed Snake (*Leptodeira septentrionalis*)   Photo: Troy Hibbitts

Cat-Eyed Snake

Leptodeira septentrionalis
Protected by law in TX
Mildly Venomous

Species: There is one species of Cat-eyed Snake occurring within the U.S., the Northern Cat-eyed Snake (*Leptodeira septentrionalis*).

History: The genus *Leptodeira* was described by Leopold Fitzinger in 1843 and the Northern Cat-Eyed Snake (*Leptodeira septentrionalis*) was described by Robert Kennicott, in a paper by Spencer Baird in 1859.

Other Common Names: Annulated Snake, Banded cat-eyed snake, Bush Snake, Cat-eyed Night Snake, Machete Savane, and Nocturnal Tree Snake.

Size: Small to medium. Adults average 18–24 in. (45.7–61 cm), but the record is 38¾ in. (98.4 cm).

Identification: Smooth-scaled.   Vertical, cat-like pupils. This is a cream, yellowish, orangish to reddish snake with 30–39 brown to blackish body blotches or bands that are lightly speckled with orange color. Neck is rather narrow, and the head is broad, with the snout and top of head brownish.

Brood Size: Egg-layer. Lays 6–12 eggs from March to May.

Range: Extreme southeastern and southern (Rio Grande Valley) Texas, and south into northeastern Mexico.

Prey: Feeds on amphibians, such as frogs, toads, and tadpoles, as well as occasionally on snakes, lizards, and mice.

Habitat: Terrestrial. In the U.S. this species is generally found near water in sub-tropical, semi-desert, thorn savannah, riparian, or coastal plain habitats.   Often climbs into bushes.

Notes: Has enlarged grooved teeth at rear of jaw for injecting mild venom into prey.   This snake is large enough that it might cause harm to a human if allowed to swallow a finger far enough to bring these teeth into play. It is probably a good idea not to test this theory, and to not be bitten at all. Its habitat in the U.S. is shrinking due to expansion of cities and farms in south Texas.

Red Coachwhip (*Masticophis flagellum piceus*).   Photo: David Jahn

Whipsnakes
Masticophis flagellum, Masticophis lateralis,
Masticophis taeniatus, Masticophis schotti & Masticophis bilineatus
Alameda Whipsnake (*M. l. euryxanthus*) is a Federally Protected Threatened Species
San Joaquin Coachwhip (*M. f. ruddocki*) is Protected by law in CA
Western Coachwhip (*M. f. testaceus*) is Protected by law in CO

Species & Subspecies: Whipsnakes in the western U.S. consist of five species. Four of the five species contain a total of 13 subspecies:

1) The Coachwhip (*Masticophis flagellum*): San Joaquin Coachwhip (*Masticophis flagellum ruddocki*) Brattstrom and Warren, 1953; Red Coachwhip (*Masticophis flagellum piceus*) Cope, 1892; Western Coachwhip (*Masticophis flagellum testaceus*) Say, in James, 1823; Eastern Coachwhip (*Masticophis flagellum flagellum*) Shaw, 1802; Lined Coachwhip (*Masticophis flagellum lineatulus)* (Smith, 1941); Sonoran Coachwhip (*Masticophis flagellum cingulum*) Lowe and Woodin, 1954; and Baja California Coachwhip (*Masticophis flagellum fuliginosus*) Cope, 1895.
2) The Sonoran Whipsnake (*Masticophis bilineatus*).
3) The Striped Whipsnake (*Masticophis taeniatus*): Desert Striped Whipsnake (*Masticophis taeniatus taeniatus*) Hallowell, 1852 and Central Texas Whipsnake (*Masticophis taeniatus girardi*) Stejneger and Barbour, 1917.
4) Schott's Whipsnake (*Masticophis schotti*): Schott's Whipsnake (*Masticophis schotti schotti*) and Ruthven's Whipsnake (*Masticophis schotti ruthveni*) Ortenburger, 1923.

Range Maps
Left: Coachwhips-San Joaquin (Maroon), Red (Blue), Baja (Brown), Sonoran (Yellow), Western (Green), Lined (Lavender), & Eastern (Pink).
Right: Chaparral (Blue), Alameda (Yellow), Desert Striped (Brown), Central Texas (Green), Schott's (Lavender), & Ruthven's (Maroon).

5) The California Whipsnake (*Masticophis lateralis*): Chaparral Whipsnake (*Masticophis lateralis lateralis*) Hallowell, 1853 and Alameda Whipsnake (*Masticophis lateralis euryxanthus*) Riemer, 1954 (Fed. Threatened).

History: The Coachwhip (*Masticophis flagellum*) was described by George Shaw in 1802, the Sonoran Whipsnake (*Masticophis bilineatus*) was described by Giorgio Jan in 1863, the Desert Whipsnake (*Masticophis taeniatus*) was described by Edward Hallowell in 1852, the Schott's Whipsnake (*Masticophis schotti*) was described by Baird & Girard in 1853, and the California Whipsnake (*Masticophis lateralis*) was described by Edward Hallowell in 1853.

Other Common Names: These are some of the regional names given to some of the species and subspecies listed above. Not all names apply to all species: Arizona Racer, Black Whipsnake, Blotched Coachwhip, Brown Thread Viper, Eagle Pass Racer, Girard's Racer, Many-striped Whipsnake, Mountain Racer, Nasal Viper, Ornate Whipsnake, Pacific Coachwhip, Pink Racer, Pink-bellied Racer, Prairie Racer, San Francisco Racer, Striped Racer, Striped-side Whipsnake, Whiplike Nasal Viper, Whipster, White Racer, and Yellow Coachwhip.

Size: Large. Adult Coachwhips range from 36–102 in. (91–260 cm), Sonoran Whipsnakes from 24–67 in. (61–170 cm), Desert Whipsnakes from 30–72 in. (76–183 cm), Schott's Whipsnake from 40–56 in. (102–142 cm), and the California Whipsnake from 30–60 in. (76–152 cm).

Identification: Smooth scaled. Whipsnakes are slender snakes with a head that is distinctly wider than the neck (unlike Racers). The tail has a scale pattern that resembles the braiding on a whip, hence the common name. The body patterns and colors vary from species to species.

Coachwhips are generally tan, red, reddish, or grayish, with or without darker, elongate blotches (Western Coachwhip), black neck markings (Red Coachwhip), or just solid black (Red Coachwhip and Eastern Coachwhip variations). The belly is generally solid pinkish or tan.

Sonoran Whipsnake is grayish brown, olive, greenish, or bluish gray above, which becomes lighter toward the rear of the body. It has a thin white stripe (turning to yellowish on each side and a fainter stripe below just above the belly. Belly is cream turning to pale yellow toward the tail.

Desert Striped Whipsnake is black, greenish brown, tan, bluish, or olive, with two light stripes on the upper sides that are edged with black. These stripes merge into one toward the tail end of the snake. There is an additional fainter stripe below these also edged in black. The dorsal scales are usually lighter on the edges, sometimes so light as to give the impression of a speckled snake.   The belly is yellowish to cream, changing to white toward the neck and head. Underside of the tail is pink.

Central Texas Whipsnake is blackish to reddish brown, with extremely faint white side stripes like the Desert Whipsnake, but these are only visible at intervals or in "patches", being brightest on the neck and fading toward the tail. Underside of tail is pink.

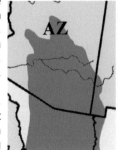

Sonoran Whipsnake Range

Schott's Whipsnake is similar to the Desert Whipsnake, but with only two side stripes (an upper and lower). It is the only strongly striped Whipsnake in southern Texas.

Ruthven's Whipsnake is olive greenish to olive brown, and usually shows no pattern or stripes except possibly along the neck. The upper body scales are faintly edged in lighter color. The Belly is bright yellow, bluish gray, and pink, graduating from one color to the next from neck to tail. Underside of tail is bright red. Throat is dotted with dark orange.

California Whipsnake is dark brown, dark olive, or blackish, with a thin white or cream stripe on each side that becomes fainter toward the tail. On the Alameda Whipsnake the stripe is wider and bright to pale orange. Belly on both is pale yellow, whitish, cream or orange. Underside of tail is pink.

Brood Size: Egg-layer. Anywhere from 3–24 eggs can be laid, depending on the species.

Range: The Coachwhips are found from the West coast to the southeastern states. The Chaparral Whipsnake and Alameda Whipsnakes are only found in California, but the other Whipsnakes have ranges that extend southeastward from Washington to Texas.

Prey: Eats insects, lizards, snakes, birds, and small mammals.

Habitat: Terrestrial. The elevational ranges for Whipsnakes are as follows: Coachwhips: below sea-level to around 8,250 feet (2,515 m), Sonoran Whipsnake: near sea-level to about 7,500 feet (2,290 m), Striped Whipsnake: sea-level to 10,100 feet (3,077 m), Schott's Whipsnake: up to 7,546 feet (2,300 m), and the California Whipsnake: sea-level to 7,400 feet (2,250 m). Whipsnakes need room to move, so are usually found in open areas, such as desert, chaparral, grassland, riparian corridors, wooded edge, and the edge of swamps, marshes, and lakes.

Notes: Whipsnakes were recently classified under the genus *Coluber* with the Racers. This has recently changed, and the Whipsnakes are now back in their historic genus of *Masticophis*. This is as it should be, as the word "mastix" is Greek for whip, and "ophis" is Greek for snake, so this scientific name better describes these whip-like creatures.

Baja Coachwhip (*Masticophis flagellum fuliginosus*). Photo: Sam Murray

Western Coachwhip (*Masticophis flagellum testaceus*).
Photo: Brian Hubbs

Red Coachwhip (*Masticophis flagellum piceus*).
Photo: Dave Tobler

Red Coachwhip (*Masticophis flagellum piceus*) [Black Phase].
Photo: Bill Love

San Joaquin Coachwhip (*Masticophis flagellum ruddocki*).
Photo: David Jahn

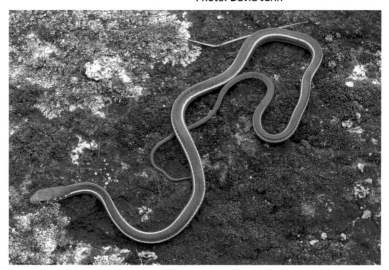

Chaparral Whipsnake (*Masticophis lateralis lateralis*).
Photo: Brian Hubbs

Alameda Whipsnake (*Masticophis lateralis euryxanthus*)
Photo: David Jahn

Desert Striped
Whipsnake
(*Masticophis taeniatus
taeniatus*)

Photo: Alan St.John

Central Texas Whipsnake (*Masticophis taeniatus girardi*)
Photo: Troy Hibbitts

Schott's Whipsnake (*Masticophis schotti schotti*)
Photo: Troy Hibbitts

Ruthven's Whipsnake (*Masticophis schotti ruthveni*).
Photo: Troy Hibbitts

Sonoran Whipsnake (*Masticophis bilineatus*).   Photo: Bill Love

Diamond-backed Watersnake (*Nerodia rhombifer*).   Photo: Brian Hubbs

Watersnakes & Salt Marsh Snakes
Nerodia erythrogaster, Nerodia fasciata, Nerodia harteri,
Nerodia rhombifer, Nerodia sipedon & Nerodia clarkii
Harter's Watersnake (*N. harteri*) Protected by law in TX
Plain-bellied Watersnake (*N. erythrogaster*) Protected by law in NM
Northern Watersnake (*N. sipedon*) Protected by law in CO

Species & Subspecies: There are six species of Watersnakes and Salt Marsh Watersnakes found in the western U.S., one of which has two subspecies:
1) Salt Marsh Watersnake (*Nerodia clarkii*)
2) Plain-bellied Watersnake (*Nerodia erythrogaster*)
3) Broad-banded Watersnake (*Nerodia fasciata*)
4) Harter's Watersnake (*Nerodia harteri*)
   Brazo's River Watersnake (*Nerodia harteri harteri*) Trapido, 1941
   Concho Watersnake (*Nerodia harteri paucimaculata*) Tinkle and Conant,1961
5) Diamond-backed Watersnake (*Nerodia rhombifer*)
6) Northern Watersnake (*Nerodia sipedon*)

History: The Salt Marsh Watersnake (*Nerodia clarkii*) was described by Baird and Girard in 1853, the Plain-bellied Watersnake (*Nerodia erythrogaster*) by Johann Forster in 1771, the Broad-banded Watersnake (*Nerodia fasciata*) by Frank Blanchard in 1923, Harter's Watersnake (*Nerodia harteri*) by Harold Trapido in 1941, the Diamond-backed Watersnake (*Nerodia rhombifer*) by Edward Hallowell in 1852, and the Northern Watersnake (*Nerodia sipedon*) by Carolus Linnaeus in 1758.

Other Common Names: Banded Watersnake, Black Water Adder, Brown Water Snake, Common Watersnake, Diamond Watersnake, Moccasin, Spotted Water Adder, Water Pilot, and Water Viper.

Size: Medium to large. Adult Watersnake size ranges are as follows:
Salt Marsh Watersnake ranges from 15–30 in. (38–76 cm).
Plain-bellied Watersnake ranges from 30–62 in. (76–157 cm).
Broad-banded Watersnake ranges from 22–36 in. (56–90 cm).
Harter's Watersnake ranges from 20–30 in. (51–76 cm).
Diamond-backed Watersnake ranges from 30–48 in. (76–122 cm).
Northern Watersnake ranges from 22–53 in. (56–135 cm).

Identification: Keeled-scales. These are relatively thick-bodied serpents with scales that feel rough due to their keeled nature. Generally a brownish, reddish, greenish, or tan snake with darker blotches or diamond shapes down the back, however, when the snakes are basking and dry no pattern may be evident.

Brood Size: Live-bearing. Depending on the species, brood size can range from 2–100 young.

Range: Various species of Watersnakes are found from southeastern New Mexico and eastern Colorado east to the Atlantic Coast. See the Range Maps in this chapter for the ranges of individual species covered in this book.

Prey: Primarily fish and amphibians, but also crayfish, insects, young turtles, and small mammals.

Habitat: Aquatic. Associated with rivers, streams, ditches, marshes, lakes, bayous, and swamps. These serpents are seldom found far from water. The two western-most species are found at higher elevations than the others. The Plain-bellied Watersnake occurs from sea level to 6,700 feet (2,042 m), and the Northern Watersnake from sea level to around 5,500 feet (1,676 m).

Notes: Recently, the Harter's Watersnakes have been split into two different species, but in this guide they are still listed as subspecies of the same species. The Concho Watersnake is an Endangered Species program success story. Like the American Alligator in 1987, it was recently removed from the list of U.S. endangered species due to recovery and abundance in the wild.

Salt Marsh Watersnake
Range

Plain-bellied Watersnake
Range

Broad-banded Watersnake
Range

Harter's Watersnakes:
Brazo's (Blue)
Concho (Red)

Diamond-backed
Watersnake Range

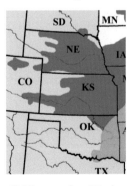

N. Watersnake (Blue)
Intergrade Zone (Gray)

Salt Marsh Watersnake (*Nerodia clarkii*).   Photo: Troy Hibbitts

Plain-bellied Watersnake (*Nerodia erythrogaster*).   Photo: Brian Hubbs

Broad-banded Watersnake (*Nerodia fasciata*).   Photo: Phil Peak

Northern Watersnake (*Nerodia sipedon*).
Photo: Brian Hubbs

Brazo's River Watersnake (*Nerodia harteri harteri*).   Photo: Troy Hibbitts

Juvenile Plain-bellied
Watersnake (*Nerodia
erythrogaster*)

Photo: Bill Love

Green Snakes

Opheodrys vernalis & Opheodrys aestivus

Rough Green Snake (*Opheodrys aestivus*).   Photo: Phil Peak

Smooth Green Snake (*O. vernalis*) is

Protected by law in CO, NE, TX, & UT

Species & Subspecies: Two species of Green Snakes, the Rough Green Snake (*Opheodrys aestivus*) and the Smooth Green Snake (*Opheodrys vernalis*) occur within the western U.S. One of the species has two subspecies, with the Northern Rough Green Snake (*Opheodrys aestivus aestivus*) being found in the West.

History: The Rough Green Snake (*Opheodrys aestivus*) was described by Carolus Linnaeus in 1766, while the Smooth Green Snake (*Opheodrys vernalis*) was described by Richard Harlan in 1827.

Other Common Names: Green Bush Snake, Green Whipsnake, Huckleberry Snake, Keel-scale Green Snake, Magnolia Snake, Smooth Grass Snake, and Vine Snake (for Rough Green Snake). Garden Snake, Grass Snake, Green Grass Snake, Spring Snake, and Summer Snake (for Smooth Green Snake).

Size: Small. Adult Smooth Green Snakes are 11–20 in. (28–51 cm), with a record of 26 in. (66 cm). Adult Rough Green Snakes are a little larger, averaging 22–32 in. (56–81 cm), with a record of 45 in. (114 cm).

Identification: The Rough Green Snake has keeled scales, while the Smooth Green Snake has smooth scales. Both are green above, and pale whitish, greenish, or
yellowish

Rough Green Snake
Range

Smooth Green Snake
Range

below. Rough Green Snake young are grayish green, while Smooth Green Snake young are olive to bluish gray.   Often confused with the Eastern Yellow-bellied Racer, but the young of racers are blotched.

Brood Size: Egg layers. The Smooth Green Snake lays 2–12 eggs, often spread over two clutches. The Rough Green Snake is known to lay 2–14 eggs.

Range: In the West, the Smooth Green Snake is primarily found in disjunct populations from southeastern Idaho and eastern Montana, south and east in Utah, Colorado, Wyoming, Montana, South Dakota, North Dakota, Nebraska, Kansas, and Texas.   The Smooth Green Snake has only recently been discovered to occur in northern Kansas, and will undoubtedly be revealed in more places as time passes and further exploration takes place.

The Rough Green Snake has a more continuous range from central and southeastern Texas through eastern Oklahoma and Kansas, and on eastward to the Atlantic states (central New Jersey and south).

Prey: Both Green Snakes are insect eaters, but spiders, snails, and frogs are also taken.

Habitat: Terrestrial. Rough Green Snakes prefer dense vegetation near water, but can also be found in prairie and desert situations in west Texas. In the West, the Smooth Green Snake is more of an upland inhabitant, but occupies lowlands in the north-central and southern part of the country. It prefers marshes, meadows, stream edge, and open woods from near sea-level to 9,500 feet (2,900 m).

Notes: Good climbers, the Green Snakes spend a great deal of time in bushes, where they blend with the leaves as they search for insect prey.

Smooth Green Snake (*Opheodrys vernalis*).   Photo: Matt Cage

The Brown Vine Snake (*Oxybelis aeneus*).   Photo: Bill Love

Brown Vine Snake

Oxybelis aeneus
Mildly Venomous

Species: The Brown Vine Snake (*Oxybelis aeneus*).

History: The Brown Vine Snake (*Oxybelis aeneus*) was first described by Johann Georg Wagler in 1824.

Other Common Names: Arizona Long-headed Snake, Arizona Vine Snake, Bush Snake, Horse-whip Snake, Pike-headed Snake, Pike-headed Tree Snake, and Vine Snake.

Size: Medium to large (Long). Adults range from 36–60 in. (91–152 cm).

Identification: Smooth-scaled. A very thin snake with a long, narrow, pointed snout. Gray or grayish brown with dark flecking at mid-body. Belly is plain gray. Chin and throat are yellowish to white. Dark eye stripe.

Brood Size: Egg-layer. Clutches of 3–8 eggs have been documented, laid in summer. Hatching in Arizona occurs in September.

Range: In the U.S. this snake is only known from the Atascosa, Pajarito, and Patagonia Mountains in Arizona. Unconfirmed sightings and reports exist for the Baboquivari and Santa Rita Mountains.

Prey: Eats primarily lizards, but frogs, fish, and insects are also known to be taken.

Habitat: Terrestrial. Found from sea-level to about 8,200 feet (2,500 m). In Arizona this snake is found on brushy or grassy hillsides, and along stream bottoms, often in bushes or small trees.

Notes: This is a mildly venomous snake that injects venom into prey from enlarged grooved teeth in the rear of the upper jaw. It can cause immediate pain and numbness around the bitten area in humans that may last for 12 or more hours. It is not a good idea to handle this snake carelessly. When threatened or held it will often gape its jaws and expose the black interior of the mouth and throat.

Juvenile Great Plains Ratsnake (*Pantherophis emoryi*).
Photo: Matt Cage

Ratsnakes & Foxsnakes

Pantherophis bairdi, Pantherophis emoryi, Pantherophis obsoletus,
Pantherophis vulpinus, Bogertophis subocularis & Senticolis triaspis
Green Ratsnake (*S. triaspis*) Protected by law in New Mexico
Great Plains Ratsnake (*P. emoryi*) Protected by law in UT

Genera, Species & Subspecies: There are three recognized genera of Ratsnakes and Foxsnakes in the western U.S. and six species. These are the Baird's Ratsnake (*Pantherophis bairdi*), Great Plains Ratsnake (*Pantherophis emoryi*), Black Ratsnake (*Pantherophis obsoletus*), Western Foxsnake (*Pantherophis vulpinus*), Trans-Pecos Ratsnake (*Bogertophis subocularis*), and Green Ratsnake (*Senticolis triaspis*).   The Black Ratsnake (*Pantherophis obsoletus*) has two subspecies that occur in the west:
Black Ratsnake (*Pantherophis obsoletus obsoletus*) Say, 1823
Texas Ratsnake (*Pantherophis obsoletus lindheimeri*) Baird & Girard, 1853
History: The Trans-Pecos Ratsnake (*Bogertophis subocularis*) was described by Herbert Brown in 1901, the Baird's Ratsnake (*Pantherophis bairdi*) by Henry Yarrow in 1880, Great Plains Ratsnake (*Pantherophis emoryi*) by Baird & Girard in 1853, Black Ratsnake (*Pantherophis obsoletus*) by Thomas Say in 1823, Foxsnake (*Pantherophis vulpinus*) by Baird & Girard in 1853, and the Green Ratsnake (*Senticolois triaspis*) by Edward Cope in 1866 (the subspecies *Senticolois triaspis intermedia* occurs in the U.S., and was described by Oskar Boettger in 1883).
Other Common Names: Baird's Coluber, Baird's Pilot Snake, and Great Bend Ratsnake (for Baird's Ratsnake); Brown Ratsnake, Chicken Snake, Emory's Coluber, Emory's Pilot Snake, and Spotted Mouse Snake (for Great Plains Ratsnake); Black Chicken Snake, Black Pilot Snake, Black Snake, Chicken Snake, Mountain Pilot Snake, Pilot Snake, Rusty Snake, Schwartze Schlange, Sleepy John, and White-throated Racer (for Black Ratsnake); Chicken Snake, Fox Racer, Fox's Black Snake, Hardwood Rattler,   Pine Snake,   Prairie Fox Snake, and Timber Snake (for Western Foxsnake); Davis Mountain Ratsnake and Davis Mountain Pilot Snake (for Trans-Pecos Ratsnake); Mexican Green

Ratsnake and Mexican Green Snake (for Green Ratsnake).

Size: Large. Adult Baird's Ratsnakes average 33–54 in. (84–137 cm), with a record size of 62 in. (157.5 cm); Great Plains Ratsnakes average 24–36 in. (61–91 cm), with a record size of 60 in. (152 cm); Black Ratsnakes average 42–72 in. (106.7–183 cm), with a record size of 101 in. (256.5 cm); Texas Ratsnakes average 42–72 in. (106.7–183 cm), with a record size of 86 in. (218.4 cm); Western Foxsnakes average 36–54 in. (91–137 cm), with a record size of 70½ in. (179 cm); Trans-Pecos Ratsnakes average 34–54 in. (86 –137 cm), with a record size of 66 in. (167.6 cm); and Green Ratsnakes are 24–50 in. (61–127 cm).

Identification: Weakly keeled-scales. All Ratsnakes have rather elongated heads. The *Baird's Ratsnake* is a grayish brown snake with orange and gray coloration on the sides (either intense or muted), and a dark stripe on the upper sides and a lighter, less distinct darker stripe on the lower sides. The head is orangish-brown. Young have 48 or more dark crossbands on a mostly gray or grayish brown ground color. The belly is light orange with darker blotches or squares of orange along the edges.

The *Great Plains Ratsnake* is light brown, tan, or grayish brown with 48–73 darker brown crossbands or blotches on the back. There are a pair of dark, elongated neck blotches that unite on top of the head to resemble a spear point. Belly is light gray with a row of darker half-moon shapes along each edge, turning to blotches toward the tail. Young are patterned like adults, only the botches are darker and more distinct.

The *Black Ratsnake* is usually overall black in color, but in some regions a pattern of dark blotches separated by lighter areas is visible. Head is dark above, with white chin and lips. The belly is diffused with gray or brown on white or yellowish coloration. Young have a strong pattern of dark blotches on a grayish background, which darkens with age to the almost all black adult pattern.

The *Texas Ratsnake* is a gray or yellowish snake with 25–34 blotches of dark brown, charcoal, or gray on the back. Smaller dark blotches along the lower sides fuse together to form a lengthwise stripe. Head is dark above, with white chin and lips. Young have very distinct darker blotches on a gray ground color.

The *Western Foxsnake* is a distinctly dark brown blotched snake with a ground color of tan, yellowish, or light brown. Blotches are usually dark chocolate brown, with smaller blotches on each side and an average of 41 large blotches down the back. Head can be brownish or reddish. The belly is usually yellow and checkered with black. Young are whitish-gray with black blotches.

The *Trans-Pecos Ratsnake* is known as the "H" snake, due to its pattern of 27–41 dark "H" shaped markings. Ground color is tan, yellowish, grayish, or light brown, with a pair of dark black stripes beginning on the neck and continuing to about mid-body. At intervals the stripes widen, and a portion of the gap between the stripes is filled with black and brown (creating the "H" shape). Once the stripes cease, the "H" shapes continue at intervals to the tip of the tail. Head is solid tan, large compared to neck, and the eyes are large. Neck and throat are white, with belly being olive-buff or whitish. A "Blonde" morph exists in the wild that has a much more faded pattern.

The *Green Ratsnake* is an unmarked green, grayish-green, or olive snake with a white chin and unmarked belly of whitish or cream. Young have a series of transverse (tilted crosswise) blotches along the back, which fade with age into the all green pattern.

Brood Size: Egg-layers. The Baird's Ratsnake lays up to 10 eggs, the Great Plains Ratsnake lays 3–37 eggs, the Black Ratsnake lays from 12–20 eggs, the Western Foxsnake lays 15–20 eggs, the Trans-Pecos Ratsnake lays 3–7 eggs, and the Green Ratsnake lays 2–7eggs.

Range: The Ratsnakes, depending on species, are found from eastern Utah to the Atlantic states and south to southern Texas. Western Foxsnakes occur from eastern Nebraska, southeastern South Dakota, and northwestern Missouri eastward through western, central and eastern Iowa, southern Minnesota most of Wisconsin, and northern Illinois and western Indiana. See Range Maps for exact ranges of each.

Prey: Ratsnakes and Foxsnakes eat rodents, birds, and lizards.

Habitat: Terrestrial. Baird's Ratsnake and Trans-Pecos Ratsnakes prefer arid and semi-arid habitats such as in the Chihuahuan Desert region to around 5,250 feet (1,600 m); the Great Plains Ratsnake is found in grassland, canyons, juniper forest, deciduous forest edge, valleys, and rocky hillsides to 7,218 feet (2,200 m); the Black Ratsnake is predominantly associated with river valleys, forest, and forest edge; the Western Foxsnake prefers woodlands, farmland, prairies, valleys, and dunes; and the Green Ratsnake is a resident of arid to montane areas from near sea-level to around 7,000 feet (2,130 m) in association with ocotillo, chaparral, pine-oak woodland, and thornscrub.

Notes: Constrictors. Great Plains Ratsnakes, Black Ratsnakes, and to some extent Foxsnakes are notorious for being ill tempered biters. The bite is as harmless as a scrape or cut, but if the snake is warm at all you can expect to be bitten repeatedly in quick succession if you pick one up. However, they usually tame down rather quickly with repeated gentle handling.

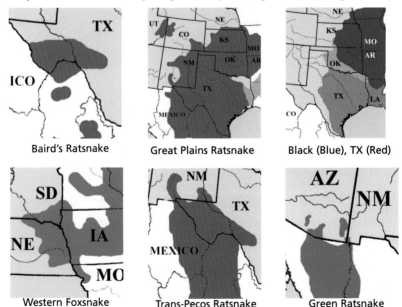

| Baird's Ratsnake | Great Plains Ratsnake | Black (Blue), TX (Red) |
| Western Foxsnake | Trans-Pecos Ratsnake | Green Ratsnake |

Baird's Ratsnake (*Pantherophis bairdi*).   Photo: Bill Love

Trans-Pecos Ratsnake (*Bogertophis subocularis*). Photo: Troy Hibbitts

Green Ratsnake (*Senticolis triaspis*).   Photo: Sam Murray

Black Ratsnake (*Pantherophis o. obsoletus*).   Photo: Matt Cage

Texas Ratsnake (*Pantherophis o. lindheimeri*).   Photo: Troy Hibbitts

Western Foxsnake (*Pantherophis vulpinus*).
Photo: Bill Love

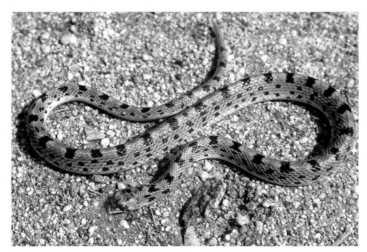

Spotted Leaf-nosed Snake (*Phyllorhynchus decurtatus*).　　Photo: Brian Hubbs

Leaf-nosed Snakes
Phyllorhynchus decurtatus & Phyllorhynchus browni

Species: Two species are found in the West, the Saddled Leaf-nosed Snake (*Phyllorhynchus browni*) and Spotted Leaf-nosed Snake (*Phyllorhynchus decurtatus*).

History: The Saddled Leaf-nosed Snake (*Phyllorhynchus browni*) was described by Leonhard Hess Stejneger in 1890, while the Spotted Leaf-nosed Snake (*Phyllorhynchus decurtatus*) was described by Edward Cope in 1868.

Other Common Names: Brown's Flat-nosed Snake, Brown's Leaf-nosed Snake, Maricopa Leaf-nosed Snake, and Pima Leaf-nosed Snake (for Saddled Leaf-nosed Snake). Clouded Leaf-nosed Snake, Cloudy Leaf-nosed Snake, Desert Leaf-nosed Snake, and Leaf-nosed Snake (for Spotted Leaf-nosed Snake).

Size: Adults of both Leaf-nosed Snake species are 12–20 in. (30–51 cm).

Identification: Smooth-scaled. Both have a triangular-shaped enlarged scale on the snout that appears to be raised above the rest of the scales. The Saddled Leaf-nosed Snake is pink or cream colored with fewer than 17 darker brown, elongate blotches or saddles down the back. The belly is white with no markings. The Spotted Leaf-nosed Snake is pink, tan, gray, or yellowish, with more than 17 brown blotches on the back. The belly is white with no markings.

Leaf-nosed Snake Ranges

Saddled Leaf-nosed Snake (Left).

Spotted Leaf-nosed Snake (Right)

Brood Size: Egg-layer. Both species lay from 2–6 eggs in summer.

Range: The Saddled Leaf-nosed Snake is found from the vicinity of Tucson, Arizona west to Organ Pipe National Monument, and north to the Phoenix-Superior, Arizona region. The Spotted Leaf-nosed Snake has a larger range, being found from south-central and southwestern Arizona to southern Sonora and Baja California Sur, and northward to Inyo County, California.

Prey: Both species eat lizards and their eggs.

Habitat: Terrestrial. Both species are secretive burrowers. The Saddled Leaf-nosed Snake prefers loose, rocky or sandy gravelly soils in desert scrub in the northern part of its range, and thornscrub and the lower edge of thornforest in the south. The Spotted Leaf-nosed Snake prefers desert areas grown to creosote bush in sandy or gravelly soils.

Saddled Leaf-nosed Snake (*Phyllorhynchus browni*).   Photo: Ben Jones

Saddled Leaf-nosed Snake (*Phyllorhynchus browni*) - Close-up of snout.
Photo: Ben Jones

Bull Snake (*Pituophis catenifer sayi*).   Photo: Brian Hubbs

Gopher Snake, Bull Snake, & Pine Snake
Pituophis catenifer & Pituophis ruthveni
Louisiana Pine Snake (*P. ruthveni*) is protected by law in Texas

Species & Subspecies: There are two species in the genus *Pituophis* that occur in the western area of the U.S., the Gopher Snakes (*Pituophis catenifer*) and Louisiana Pine Snake (*Pituophis ruthveni*). Another Pine Snake species is found in the East. In addition, six subspecies of Gopher Snake exist:
   Sonoran Gopher Snake (*Pituophis catenifer affinis*) Hallowell, 1852
   San Diego Gopher Snake (*Pituophis catenifer annectens*) Baird and Girard, 1853
   Pacific Gopher Snake (*Pituophis catenifer catenifer*) Blainville, 1835
   Great Basin Gopher Snake (*Pituophis catenifer deserticola*) Stejneger, 1893
   Santa Cruz Island Gopher Snake (*Pituophis catenifer pumilus*) Klauber, 1946
   Bullsnake (*Pituophis catenifer sayi*) Schlegel, 1837
History: The species *Pituophis catenifer* was described by M. H. De Blainville in 1835, while *Pituophis ruthveni* was described by Olive Griffith Stull in 1929.
Other Common Names: Blow Snake, Coast Gopher Snake, Churchill's Bull Snake, Hisser, Oregon Bull Snake, Pacific Pine Snake, Western Bull Snake,

Bull, Gopher, & Pine Snake Ranges

Sonoran Gopher Snake (Orange)
San Diego Gopher Snake (Blue)
Pacific Gopher Snake (Yellow)
Great Basin Gopher Snake (Maroon)
Santa Cruz Island Gopher Snake (Brown)
Bull Snake (Green)
Louisiana Pine Snake (Black)
Intergrade areas (Gray)

Western Gopher Snake, Western Pine Snake, Yellow Gopher Snake.

Size: Large. Adult Bullsnakes and Gopher Snakes are from 30–110 in. (76–279 cm), while the Louisiana Pine Snake averages 48–64 in. (122–163 cm) with a record size of just over 70 in. (178 cm).

Identification: Keeled-scales. All of these snakes are characterized by a light brown, yellowish, or tan ground color with darker brown, reddish-brown or black blotches. The belly is yellowish with dark spots. Occasionally, Gopher Snakes will be partially or fully striped with the darker color. This morph is fairly common in portions of north-central California. Blotch counts are as follows for the Gopher Snakes: Sonoran: 34–63, San Diego: 65–106, Pacific: 47–90, Great Basin: 43–71, Santa Cruz Island: 64–82, and Bullsnake: 33–66. The Louisiana Pine Snake has 28–42 blotches.

Brood Size: Egg-layer. Bullsnakes and Gopher Snakes lay from 2–24 eggs, while the Louisiana Pine Snake lays only 3–5 eggs.

Range: Gopher snakes are found from the West Coast to the Rocky Mountains, except at the higher elevations and in western Washington. Bullsnakes continue the range beyond the Rocky Mountains and are found throughout the Midwest as far as eastern Missouri, northwestern Illinois, and southwestern Wisconsin, but are absent from much of Minnesota and North Dakota. Isolated populations occur in Indiana. Louisiana Pine Snakes are found (or were formerly found) in eastern Texas and west-central Louisiana.

Prey: These are primarily rodent eaters, but lizards and birds and their eggs are also taken.

Habitat: Terrestrial. Bullsnakes and Gopher Snakes prefer open grassland and desert habitats, but can also be found in canyons, forest, chaparral covered hillsides, and high mountain situations from below sea-level to over 9,100 feet (2,773+ m). The Louisiana Pine Snake prefers sandy, long-leaf pine forests.

Notes: Constrictors. One of the few snakes that hiss loudly and strike when provoked or startled. Bullsnakes and Gopher Snakes are common to abundant, however the Louisiana Pine Snake appears to be getting scarce over much of its range.

Sonoran Gopher Snake (*Pituophis catenifer affinis*).   Photo: Ben Jones

Pacific Gopher Snake (*Pituophis catenifer catenifier*).

Photo: Brian Hubbs

Great Basin Gopher Snake (*Pituophis catenifer deserticola*).
Photo: Alan St. John

Juvenile Pacific Gopher Snake (*Pituophis catenifer catenifer*).
Photo: Brian Hubbs

Louisiana Pine Snake (*Pituophis ruthveni*).   Photo: Bill Love

Typical adult San Diego
Gopher Snake (*Pituophis
catenifer annectans*).

Photo: Brian Hubbs

Juvenile San Diego Gopher
Snake (*Pituophis catenifer
annectans*) from near the
intergrade zone with the
Pacific Gopher Snake.

Photo: Brian Hubbs

Graham's Crayfish Snake (*Regina grahamii*).   Photo: Brian Hubbs

Crayfish Snakes
Regina grahamii & Regina rigida
Glossy Crayfish Snake (*R.. rigida*) protected by law in OK

Species: Two species occur within the scope of this book, the Glossy Crayfish Snake (*Regina rigida*) and Graham's Crayfish Snake (*Regina grahamii*).

History: Graham's Crayfish Snake (*Regina grahamii*) was described by Baird and Girard in 1853, while the Glossy Crayfish Snake (*Regina rigida*) was described by Thomas Say in 1825.

Other Common Names: Arkansas Water Snake, Brown Water Snake (*R. rigida*), Crawfish Snake, Graham's Leather Snake, Graham's Snake, Graham's Water Snake, Holbrook's Water Snake (*R. rigida*), Prairie Water Adder, Prairie Water Snake, Rigid Queen Snake (*R. rigida*), Stiff Snake (*R. rigida*), Striped Moccasin, Two-lined Water Snake (*R. rigida*).

Size: Small to medium. Adult Graham's Crayfish Snakes range from 18–28 in. (45.7–71 cm) with a record size of 47 in. (119.4 cm). Adult Glossy Crayfish Snakes range from 14–24 in. (36–61 cm) with a record size of 31⅜ in. (79.7 cm).

Identification: Keeled-scales. A two-toned snake. Graham's Crayfish Snake is olive, greenish-gray, or brownish on top, with a lighter, broad stripe down

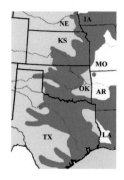

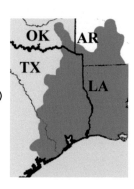

Crayfish Snake Ranges

Graham's Crayfish Snake (Left) and Glossy Crayfish Snake (Right)

the middle of the back. The lower sides are yellowish. The belly is olive.

The Glossy Crayfish Snake is a shiny brown or olive snake with an orangish or yellowish throat and orange to pinkish belly. There is a double row of dark crescent or triangular shapes the length of the belly.

Brood Size: Live-bearing. Graham's gives birth to 10–15 young, while the Glossy species gives birth to 6–13.

Range: Graham's Crayfish Snake is primarily found from southeastern Nebraska south through the eastern half of Kansas, central and eastern Oklahoma and Texas to Louisiana, Arkansas, western Missouri and most of Iowa. The Glossy Crayfish Snake is found in eastern Texas, extreme southeastern Oklahoma, southern Arkansas, and most of Louisiana.

Prey: As the name suggests, crayfish and other crustaceans are the favored prey, especially freshly molted crayfish, but also takes small amphibians and fish.

Habitat: Aquatic. Prefers habitat along the edge of streams, bogs, ponds, bayous, ditches, etc.

Notes: Both species were once thought to be rare until herpetologists discovered how to find these secretive snakes. Glossy Crayfish Snakes are highly aquatic, extremely secretive, and seldom seen.

Glossy Crayfish Snake (*Regina rigida*).   Photo: Bill Love

Glossy Crayfish Snake (*Regina rigida*) showing belly (venter).
Photo: Bill Love

Long-nosed Snake (*Rhinocheilus lecontei*).   Photo: David Jahn

Long-nosed Snake
Rhinocheilus lecontei
Protected by law in CO & KS

Species: The Long-nosed Snake (*Rhinocheilus lecontei*).   There are no subspecies of the Long-nosed Snake recognized at this time.

History: The Long-nosed Snake (*Rhinocheilus lecontei*) was described by Baird and Girard in 1853.

Other Common Names: Belle Snake, Desert Long-nosed Snake, LeConte's Snake, Scale-nosed Snake, and Sharp-nosed Snake.

Size: Medium. Adults are 20–60 in. (51–152 cm).

Identification: Smooth-scaled. This is a black and red banded snake that superficially resembles the Mountain Kingsnakes, and is often confused with those. There are white spots or short lines within the roughly 18–38 black bands, and black spots within the red bands along the sides, giving the snake a salt and peppered look. The red bands are actually not solid red, but consist of red-centered scales of varying degree. The red may be absent on the upper back and replaced with cream between the black bands. Occasionally these snakes lack red coloration (Clarus morph) and are only black and white (or cream). The belly is solid yellow or whitish.

Range of the Long-nosed Snake

Brood Size: Egg layer. From 4–11 eggs are laid, usually from June to August. Sometimes lays two clutches a year.

Range: From central valley, coastal southern California, and foothills of western Sierra Nevada eastward to Kansas and central and south Texas, including lower elevation areas of Arizona, western Utah, southwest Idaho (Snake River) New Mexico, southeast Colorado, and western Oklahoma.

Prey: Eats lizards and their eggs, small snakes, small mammals, and occasionally birds.

Habitat: Terrestrial. Below sea-level to over 6,000 feet (1,828 m). Found in desert, grassland, prairie, chaparral, and oak-woodland areas, usually below the level of Mountain Kingsnake occupation. Primarily a snake of arid lands, but in California it ranges to around 2,000 feet (610 m) in the foothills of the western Sierra Nevada within oak woodland and grassland habitat. In the coastal counties it occurs primarily in chaparral.

Notes: Constrictors. Long-nosed Snakes are related to the kingsnakes. There used to be two subspecies within the western U.S., but the Texas subspecies was dropped in 2004 due to a detailed morphological study. Due to the coloration, this snake could possibly be confused with the venomous Coral Snakes, but actually looks nothing like them. Coral Snakes have solidly colored bands of red, black, and yellow or white that are very distinct, red rings that always border the yellow or white rings and a solid black snout (See my book *A Guide to the Rattlesnakes and other Venomous Serpents of the United States* for detailed descriptions and photos of all the Coral Snakes.)

Long-nosed Snake
(*Rhinocheilus lecontei*).

Photo: Alan St. John

Typical (Right) and Clarus (Left) morphs of Long-nosed Snakes.

Photo: Brian Hubbs

Big Bend Patch-nosed Snake (*Salvadora hexalepis deserticola*).
Photo: Dave Tobler

Patch-nosed Snakes
Salvadora grahamiae & Salvadora hexalepis

Species & Subspecies: Two species are currently recognized, the Western Patch-nosed Snake (*Salvadora hexalepis*) and Mountain Patch-nosed Snake (*Salvadora grahamiae*), which have six subspecies between them:

Big Bend Patch-nosed Snake (*Salvadora hexalepis deserticola*) Schmidt, 1940
Desert Patch-nosed Snake (*Salvadora hexalepis hexalepis*) Cope, 1866
Mohave Patch-nosed Snake (Salvadora hexalepis mojavensis) Bogert, 1945
Coast Patch-nosed Snake (*Salvadora hexalepis virgultea*) Bogert, 1935
Mountain Patch-nosed Snake (*Salvadora g. grahamiae*) Baird and Girard, 1853
Texas Patch-nosed Snake (*Salvadora grahamiae lineata*) Schmidt, 1940

History: The genus *Salvadora* was described by Baird and Girard in 1853, as was the species *Salvadora grahamiae*. *Salvadora hexalepis* was described by Edward Cope in 1866.
Other Common Names: Arizona Flat-nosed Snake, Flat-nosed Snake, Striped Mouse Snake, and Whip Snake.
Size: Medium to large. Adult Western Patch-nosed Snakes are 20–46 in. (51–117 cm), and adult Mountain Patch-nosed Snakes are 22–47 in. (56–119 cm).
Identification: Smooth-scaled. Patch-nosed Snakes are slender like Racers or Whipsnakes, with an enlarged patch-like raised scale on the snout. This scale is similar to the snout scale on the Leaf-nosed Snakes (*Phyllorhynchus*).
The *Western Patch-nosed Snakes* are tan, brown, yellowish, pinkish, or gray with a wide pinkish, orangish, or tan stripe down the back that is bordered on each side by a dark brown or blackish stripe that begins behind each eye. These stripes are broad on the Coast Patch-nosed Snake and narrower on the Desert, Big Bend, and Mohave Patch-nosed Snakes, which usually have an additional thin black stripe lower on the sides. The belly is usually plain

white, turning to pinkish on the tail.

The *Mountain Patch-nosed Snake* is similar, but normally lacks the side stripe. The dark upper stripes are much bolder in appearance and better defined. The light back stripe is whitish, yellow, orangish, or gray, and the ground color is usually gray or tan. The belly is plain whitish or yellowish, turning to pinkish on the tail.

The *Texas Patch-nosed Snake* has a thinner back stripe of yellow or pale orange, with bordering dark brown stripes of about two-scales in width. The thin dark side stripe is usually present. Ground color is tan, yellowish, grayish-olive, or pale gray. The top of the head is plain tan or olive.

Brood Size: Egg-layer. The Western Patch-nosed Snake lays 4–12 eggs, and the Mountain Patch-nosed Snake lays 5–10 eggs.

Range: The various forms of Western Patch-nosed Snakes range from northwestern Nevada and south-coastal California to the Big Bend region of Texas. The Mountain Patch-nosed Snakes are found from central (disjunct population) and southeast Arizona through most of New Mexico and south to the Trans-Pecos region of Texas. Texas Patch-nosed Snakes intergrade with the Mountain patch-nosed Snake east of the Big Bend region to about the Pecos River, and then occupy most of central and south Texas.

Prey: Eats small mammals, lizards, reptile eggs, and young birds.

Habitat: Terrestrial. The Western Patch-nosed Snake is found from below sea-level to around 7,000 feet (2,130 m), in rocky areas as well as sandy habitat within prairies, grasslands, sagebrush, juniper woodland, chaparral, and desert scrub. The Mountain Patch-nosed Snake is found from sea-level (in Texas) to over 6,500 feet (1,980 m) in rocky, rough terrain in canyons, on plateaus, and on slopes within woodland and forest in mountains. It is also found on the coastal plain in southeastern Texas within scrub and grassland habitat, as well as in central Texas in mesquite and hilly terrain.

Notes: These are fast snakes, like the Racers and Whipsnakes. They seldom sit still long enough for anyone to get a good look at them before disappearing into brush or down a rodent burrow. I photographed the Texas Patch-nosed Snake pictured in this chapter outside Brownsville, Texas as it rested under a discarded piece of plywood at a local dumping area.

Mountain Patch-nosed Snake (Blue)
Texas Patch-nosed Snake (Orange).
Intergrade Zone (Gray)

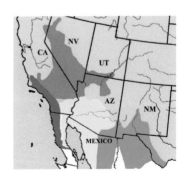

Western Patch-nosed Snake
Range
Big Bend (Green)
Desert (Yellow)
Mohave (Orange)
Coast (Blue)

Coast Patch-nosed Snake (*Salvadora hexalepis virgultea*)
Photo: Sam Murray

Mountain Patch-nosed Snake (*Salvadora g. grahamiae*).
Photo: Bill Love

Texas Patch-nosed Snake
(*Salvadora grahamiae lineata*

Photo: Brian Hubbs

Variable Groundsnake (*Sonora semiannulata semiannulata*)
Photo: David Jahn

Groundsnake

Sonora semiannulata
Protected by law in OR

Species & Subspecies: There is one species of Groundsnake in the western U.S., the Western Groundsnake (*Sonora semiannulata*), and two subspecies: Variable Groundsnake (*Sonora semiannulata semiannulata*) Baird and Girard, 1853 and Southern Texas Groundsnake (*Sonora semiannulata taylori*) Boulenger, 1894.

History: The Western Groundsnake (*Sonora semiannulata*) was first described by Baird and Girard in 1853.

Other Common Names: Arizona Earth Snake, Bi-colored Ground Snake, Blanchard's Western Ground Snake, South Texas Earth Snake, and Taylor's Snake.

Size: Small. Adults are from 8–18 in. (20.3–46 cm).

Identification: Smooth-scaled. Head is slightly wider than neck. The Variable Groundsnake can be olive, grayish, red, or orange (lighter on sides) with up to 35 black crossbands; solidly colored with tan, olive, brown, or gray; or tan, olive, brown, or gray with a faint or bright wide back stripe of orange, red, or beige. Belly can be white or yellowish with or without dark crossbands. Southern Texas Groundsnake is basically unicolored gray to medium brown.

Brood Size: Egg-layer. Lays 3–6 eggs.

Range: Found from the more arid regions of eastern California, Baja, Nevada, and southwestern Idaho and southeastern Oregon eastward through parts of Utah, most of Arizona and New Mexico to Texas, Oklahoma, southern Kansas, southwest Missouri, and northwest Arkansas. Isolated population in north-central Kansas. Southern Texas Groundsnake is found from southern Texas northeastward to north of Houston.

Prey: Eats scorpions, centipedes, spiders, crickets, grasshoppers, and insect larvae.

Variable Groundsnake (Blue) & Southern Texas Groundsnake (Red).

Habitat: Terrestrial. From sea level to about 6,000 feet (1,830 m) in arid and semi-arid regions where soil is gravelly or sandy and suitable for burrowing. Found in many types of habitat, including hillsides, riverbeds, desert flats, thornscrub, prairies, and valleys.

Notes: One of the small snakes in the west that is often confused with the venomous Coral Snake.

Variable Groundsnake (*Sonora semiannulata semiannulata*)
Photo: Matt Cage

Variable Groundsnake (*Sonora semiannulata semiannulata*)
Photo: Brian Hubbs

Texas Brownsnake (*Storeria dekayi texana*)
Photo: Brian Hubbs

Brown Snake & Red-bellied Snake

Storeria dekayi & Storeria occipitomaculata
Red-bellied Snake (*S. occipitomaculata*) Protected by law in KS & WY

Species & Subspecies: There is one species each of Brown Snake and Red-bellied Snake that occur in the western United States, and five subspecies:

1) Brown Snake (*Storeria dekayi*):
Texas Brownsnake (*Storeria dekayi texana*) Trapido, 1944
Marsh Brownsnake (*Storeria dekayi limnetes*) Anderson, 1961
2) Red-bellied Snake (*Storeria occipitomaculata*)
Florida Red-bellied Snake (*Storeria occipitomaculata obscura*) Trapido, 1944
Northern Red-bellied Snake (*Storeria occipitomaculata occipitomaculata*) Storer,1839
Black Hills Red-bellied Snake (Storeria occipitomaculata pahasapae) Smith, 1963

History: Dekay's Brownsnake (*Storeria dekayi*) was described by John Edwards Holbrook in 1836, while the Red-bellied Snake (*Storeria occipitomaculata*) was described by David Humphreys Storer in 1839. The genus name for both species is in honor of David Humphreys Storer (Storeria). The Brown Snake's were named in honor of James Edward DeKay, an early 19th Century New York naturalist.

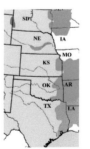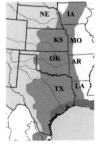

Red-bellied & Brown Snake Ranges

Other Common Names: Copper Snake, DeKay's Snake, Little Brown Snake, Red-bellied Brown Snake, Red-bellied Garter Snake, Red-bellied Dekay's Snake, Spot-necked Snake, Spotted Brown Snake, Storer's Brown Snake, and Storer's Grass Snake.

Right: Texas Brown (Red)
Marsh Brown (Blue).
Left: Florida Red-bellied (Orange)
Northern Red-bellied (Green)
Black Hills Red-bellied (Blue)

Size: Small. Adult Brown Snakes are 9–13 in. (23–33 cm), with a record size of 18 in. (46 cm). Adult Red-bellied Snakes 8–16 in. (20.3–41 cm).

Identification: Keeled-scales. *Brown Snakes* are yellowish-brown to tan, gray, or reddish with two rows of small black spots down the center of the back. The area between the spots is lighter in coloration, giving the appearance of a stripe. There is a dark spot under each eye. The belly is yellowish, pinkish, or brownish, with a small dark spot at outer edge of each scale.

Red-bellied Snakes have red bellies and an upper body color of brown, gray, or black. Three light spots are usually present on the neck just behind the head. The light stripe on the back (as in the Brown Snakes) is greatly reduced or imperceptible. Top of head is usually dark.

Brood Size: Live-bearing, Brown Snakes give birth to 3–41 (average 10–15) young from June to September, while Red-bellied Snakes give birth to 1–21 young during the same timeframe.

Range: The Texas Brown Snake occurs from southern Minnesota to Texas. The Marsh Brown Snake is found along the eastern two-thirds of the gulf coast in Texas, and all of the coast in Louisiana. The Florida Red-bellied Snake is found in extreme eastern Texas and eastward. The Northern Red-bellied Snake is found in eastern Kansas and Oklahoma, and then east across Missouri and Arkansas, and north to Canada, and eastward to the Atlantic states. Black Hills Red-bellied Snake is found in the Black Hills of Wyoming and South Dakota. There are areas of intergradations between it and the Northern Red-bellied Snake in North Dakota, Minnesota, Iowa, and Nebraska.

Prey: Prefer slugs, earthworms and other soft-bodied insects.

Habitat: Terrestrial. Sea level to high in the eastern mountains. A burrower, these snakes are seldom seen unless you look for them. Found on hillsides, along streams, in grassy valleys, sandy pine woods, moist woods, bogs, marshes, swamps, and even vacant lots within cities.

Notes: Brown Snakes are extremely common in some places and apparently declining in others. Pesticides are thought to be the cause of the declines. The young Red-bellied Snake pictured in this chapter was the first I had ever seen in Missouri, despite a dozen trips to the area and intense searches for snakes. It was found while raking thru a pile of old roofing shingles at a forest-edge dump site.

Marsh Brownsnake
(*Storeria dekayi limnetes*)

Photo: Troy Hibbitts

Northern Red-bellied Snake (*Storeria occipitomaculata occipitomaculata*) from Missouri.   Photo: Brian Hubbs

Northern Red-bellied Snake (*Storeria occipitomaculata occipitomaculata*) from Missouri (Belly view).   Photo: Brian Hubbs

Western Black-headed Snake (*Tantilla planiceps*) Photo: Dave Tobler

Black-headed & Flat-headed Snakes
Tantilla
Trans-Pecos Black-headed Snake (*T. cucullata*) Protected by law in TX
Plains Black-headed Snake (*T. nigriceps*) Protected by law in WY
Smith's Black-headed Snake (*T. hobartsmithi*) Protected by law in UT

Species: There are currently eight species of Black-headed and Flat-headed Snakes found in the West:

1) Mexican Black-headed Snake (*Tantilla atriceps*) Günther, 1895
2) Trans-Pecos Black-headed Snake (*Tantilla cucullata*) Minton, 1956
3) Smith's Black-headed Snake (*Tantilla hobartsmithi*) Taylor, 1937
4) Plains Black-headed Snake (*Tantilla nigriceps*) Kennicott, 1860
5) Western Black-headed Snake (*Tantilla planiceps*) Blainville, 1835
6) Chihuahuan Black-headed Snake (*Tantilla wilcoxi*) Stejneger, 1903
7) Yaqui Black-headed Snake (*Tantilla yaquia*) Smith, 1942
8) Flat-headed Snake (*Tantilla gracilis*) Baird and Girard, 1853

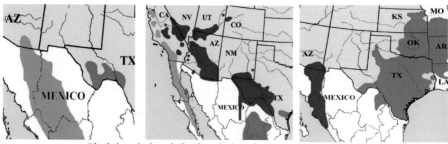
Black-headed and Flat-headed Snake Ranges

Left Map: Chihuahuan (Green), Trans-Pecos (Blue). **Center Map:** Western (Orange), Smith's (Red), & Mexican (Blue). **Right Map:** Yaqui (Red), Flat-headed (Blue).
Following page: Plains Black-headed Snake

History: The genus *Tantilla* was first described by Spencer Fullerton Baird and Charles Frédéric Girard in 1853.

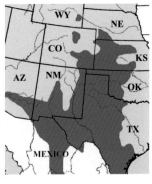

Other Common Names: Eisen's Black-head Snake and Desert Black-headed Snake (for W. Black-headed Snake); Gunther's Black-headed Snake and Texas Black-headed Snake (for Mexican Black-headed Snake); Graceful Tantilla, Hallowell's Tantilla, Miter Snake, Northern Slender Black-headed Snake, Slender Snake, Slender Tantilla, and Southern Slender Black-headed Snake (for Flat-headed Snake); Great Plains Black-headed Snake, Kennicott's Black-headed Snake, and Sand Snake (for Plains Black-headed Snake); Blanchard's Black-headed Snake, California Black-headed Snake (for Western Black-headed Snake); Utah Black-headed Snake (for Smith's Black-headed Snake); and Arizona Black-headed Snake, Arizona Tantilla, Huachuca Black-headed Snake, and Wilcox's Black-headed Snake (for Chihuahuan Black-headed Snake).

Size: Small. These snakes generally range from 5–15 in. (12.5–38 cm) in total length, with a record size of 22¾ in. (58 cm) for the Trans-Pecos Black-headed Snake.

Identification: Smooth-scaled. Ground color is grayish, tan, brown, yellowish brown, or blackish. Most have a blackish head cap, hence the name, and light ring on neck. Belly is salmon or coral red. The Flat-headed Snake does not have a dark head cap. All Black-headed Snakes look similar and the differences usually involve the placement or size of the neck band.

Brood Size: Egg-layers. Generally a clutch of 1–4 eggs are laid.

Range: The various species occupy sections of the West from California to western Nebraska, Kansas, and Missouri, and south to Texas and Mexico. See the Range Maps for specific areas for each species.

Prey: Eats centipedes, millipedes, spiders, and insects.

Habitat: Terrestrial. Smith's Black-headed Snake from near sea-level to around 6,500 feet (1,981 m), Western Black-headed Snake from sea-level to 4,000 feet (1,220 m), Chihuahuan Black-headed Snake from about 3,000 to 8,000 feet (910 to 2,440 m), Yaqui Black-headed Snake from near seal-level to about 5,500 feet (1,680 m). Habitats for the various species include coastal plain, grassland, prairie, chaparral, desert, mountain and desert canyons, woodland, and scrub. One of the few snakes that might be found under a pile of cattle dung on the prairie.

Notes: While known to have enlarged grooved teeth at rear of upper jaw, these snakes seldom attempt to bite and are not considered harmful to humans even if they do. These snakes are extremely fossorial and are seldom seen on the surface, except at night. Individuals have been found as deep as 8 feet (2.4 m) underground in Kansas during hibernation.

Trans-Pecos Black-headed Snake (*Tantilla cucullata*).

Photo: Brian Hubbs

Plains Black-headed Snake (*Tantilla nigriceps*). Photo: Matt Cage

Flat-headed Snake (*Tantilla gracilis*). Photo: Brian Hubbs

Diablo Garter Snake (*Thamnophis atratus zaxanthus*) Photo: David Jahn

Aquatic Garter Snakes & Ribbon Snakes
Thamnophis atratus, Thamnophis couchi, Thamnophis eques, Thamnophis gigas, Thamnophis hammondii, Thamnophis proximus, & Thamnophis rufipuntatus
Mexican (*T. eques*) & Narrow-headed (*T. rufipuntatus*) Garters
Protected by law in AZ & NM
Giant Garter Snake (*T. gigas*) Protected by law in CA
Western Ribbon Snake (*T. proximus*) Protected by law in NE & NM

Species: In the western U.S. there are six species of Garter Snakes and one species of Ribbon snake that are predominantly aquatic in their habits. Five of these species are also broken down into subspecies. The species and subspecies are listed below, along with those who first described them and the dates of description:

1) Aquatic Garter Snake (*Thamnophis atratus*) Kennicott, 1860
     Santa Cruz Garter Snake (*Thamnophis atratus atratus*) Kennicott, 1860
     Oregon Garter Snake (*Thamnophis atratus hydrophilus*) Fitch, 1936
     Diablo Garter Snake (*Thamnophis atratus zaxanthus*) Boundy, 1999
2) Sierra Garter Snake (*Thamnophis couchi*) Kennicott, 1859
3) Mexican Garter Snake (Thamnophis eques) Reuss, 1834
4) Giant Garter Snake (*Thamnophis gigas*) Fitch, 1940
5) Two-striped Garter Snake (*Thamnophis hammondii*) Kennicott, 1860
6) Narrow-headed Garter Snake (*Thamnophis rufipuntatus*) Cope, 1875
7) Western Ribbon Snake (*Thamnophis proximus*)
     Orange-striped Ribbon Snake (*Thamnophis proximus proximus*) Say, 1823
     Arid Land Ribbon Snake (*Thamnophis proximus diabolicus*) Rossman, 1963
     Red-striped Ribbon Snake (*Thamnophis proximus ubrilineatus*) Rossman, 1963
     Gulf Coast Ribbon Snake (*Thamnophis proximus orarius*) Rossman, 1963

History: The Garter Snake (*Thamnophis*) was first described in 1758 by Carolus Linnaeus, a Swedish zoologist who is considered the father of modern taxonomy. Later, many species were described and some broken down into subspecies as the continental U.S. was further explored by zoologists and herpetologists (See above list). Thomas Say first described the Ribbon Snake in 1823.

Other Common Names: Garden Snake, Gardner Snake, Striped Water Snake, and Water Snake.

Size: Medium. Depending on the species, these snakes can attain a maximum length of 65 inches (165 cm), but are more commonly from 20–36 inches (50.8–91 cm). A few size ranges for adults of the various species are: Aquatic Garter: 18–40 in. (46–102 cm), Giant Garter: 37–65 in. (94–165 cm), and Ribbon Snake: 18–48 in. (46–123 cm).

Identification: Moderately slender in build, with keeled scales and a head that is slightly wider than the neck. Most garter snakes are weakly or brightly striped lengthwise, either on the top of the back (dorsum) or sides (laterally), or both, however, the Narrow-headed Garter is spotted and has no stripes. Stripes can be white, yellow, orange, bluish, red, greenish, black, or gray. Ground colors (background) are normally yellow, gray, green, black, or brown. Some of the species and subspecies have a checkered or spotted pattern in addition to the striping. Checkering or spotting is usually black. The sides may also contain small, thin flecks of white. The belly is generally solidly colored with white, yellow, green, brown, gray, black, or turquoise, and may have speckling or flecks of other color present. In most species the tongue is red with a black tip. Males and females are patterned and colored similarly.

Brood Size: All species are live bearing. The Aquatic species bears from 3–12 young born from August to October, the Sierra Garter bears 5–38 from July to September, the Mexican Garter bears 7–27 from June to August, the Giant Garter bears 8–40 from July to September, and the Two-striped Garter bears 4–36 young during the summer. Ribbon Snakes bear 4–36 young also during summer.

Range: Aquatic Garter Snakes are found across the western U.S., but each species has a distinct range (shown on the range maps in this chapter), while the Ribbon Snakes are found in the central region, Texas, and eastern New Mexico.

Prey: The Aquatic species (See Habitat section below) generally prey on frogs, toads, tadpoles, fish, salamanders, newts, worms and other small aquatic or aquatic edge animals. The search for prey takes place both in the water and on shore.

Habitat: Aquatic. Sea-level to around 6,300 feet (1,920.2 m) for the Aquatic species, Sierra Garter from 300–8,000 feet (91–2,440 m), Mexican Garter from 2,000–8,500 feet (610–2,590 m), Giant Garter from sea-level to 400 feet (122 m), Two-striped Garter from sea-level to over 7,000 feet (2,134 m), Narrow-headed Garter from 2,300–7,972 feet (700–2,430 m), and Western Ribbon Snake from sea-level to around 8,000 feet (2,440 m) in Mexico. Aquatic Garter Snakes and Ribbon Snakes are very aquatic in their habits, and seldom found more than 50–100 yards from bodies of water, such as rivers, creeks, marshes, ponds, meadows, lakes, and irrigation ditches, except during hibernation.

Notes: The name, "Garter Snake", was coined because someone thought the striped pattern resembled a striped garter used to hold up women's stockings. Garter Snakes (especially females) have a nasty habit of "musking" anyone who initially restrains them, by expelling feces and musk from their anal glands. This is a defense mechanism to confuse, repel, and elude any potential predators. Anyone who has been musked by a Garter or Ribbon Snake knows how difficult it is to remove the foul smelling odor. However, with time and gentle handling this habit will almost always cease at some point.

Aquatic Garter & Ribbon Snake Ranges

Left Map: Two-striped (Blue), Narrow-headed (Red).
Center Map: Sierra (Dark Blue), Oregon (Red), Giant (Light Blue), Santa Cruz (Gray), Diablo (Green), Intergrade Zone (Orange).
Right Map: Mexican Garter (Blue).
Below Map: Orange-striped Ribbon (Red), Gulf Coast Ribbon (Yellow), Arid Land Ribbon (Blue), Red-striped (Green), Intergrade Zones (Gray).

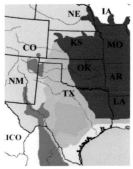

Giant Garter Snake (*Thamnophis gigas*). Photo: J.P. Stephenson

Giant Garter Snake
(*Thamnophis gigas*).
Red morph.

Photo: Richard Porter

Oregon Garter Snake (*Thamnophis atratus hydrophilus*).
Photo: David Jahn

Two-striped Garter
Snake (*Thamnophis
hammondi*).

Photo: Brian Hubbs

Santa Cruz Garter Snake (*Thamnophis atratus atratus*).
Photo: Brian Hubbs

Sierra Garter Snake (*Thamnophis couchi*).
Photo: Brian Hubbs

Mexican Garter Snake (*Thamnophis* eques).   Photo: Bill Love

Narrow-headed Garter Snake (*Thamnophis rufipuntatus*).
Photo: Brian Hubbs

Orange-striped Ribbon Snake (*Thamnophis proximus proximus*).
Photo: Brian Hubbs

Gulf Coast Ribbon Snake (*Thamnophis proximus orarius*).
Photo: Brian Hubbs

Checkered Garter Snake (*Thamnophis marcianus*) Photo: Brian Hubbs

Terrestrial Garter Snakes

Thamnophis cyrtopsis, Thamnophis elegans, Thamnophis radix,
Thamnophis marcianus, & Thamnophis ordinoides
Wandering Garter Snake (*T. e. vagrans*) protected by law in OK
Checkered Garter Snake (*T. marcianus*) Protected by law in KS

Species: In the western U.S. there are five species of Terrestrial Garter Snakes, with two species containing subspecies. These are as follows:

1) Black-necked Garter Snake (*Thamnophis cyrtopsis*) Kennicott, 1860
    Western Black-necked Garter Snake (*Thamnophis cyrtopsis cyrtopsis*) Kennicott, 1860
    Eastern Black-necked Garter Snake (*Thamnophis cyrtopsis ocellatus*) Cope, 1880
2) Terrestrial Garter Snake (*Thamnophis elegans*) Baird & Girard, 1853
    Coast Garter Snake (*Thamnophis elegans terrestris*) Fox, 1951
    Mountain Garter Snake (*Thamnophis elegans elegans*) Baird & Girard, 1853
    Wandering Garter Snake (*Thamnophis elegans vagrans*) Baird & Girard, 1853
3) Checkered Garter Snake (*Thamnophis marcianus*) Baird & Girard, 1853
4) Northwestern Garter Snake (*Thamnophis ordinoides*) Baird & Girard, 1852
5) Plains Garter Snake (*Thamnophis radix*) Baird & Girard, 1853

History: The Garter Snake (*Thamnophis*) was first described by Carolus Linnaeus in 1758. The describers of the various species covered by this chapter can be seen in the species list above.

Other Common Names: Garden Snake, Gardner Snake, Striped Water Snake, and Water Snake

Size: The Black-necked Garter: 16–46 in. (40.6–116.8 cm), Terrestrial Garter: 18–43 in. (46–109 cm), Checkered Garter: 13–42 in. (33–106.7 cm), Northwestern Garter: 13–38 in. (33–96.5 cm), and Plains Garter: 14–42 in. (35.6–106.7 cm).

Identification: Moderately slender in build, with keeled scales and a head that is slightly wider than the neck. Most garter snakes are weakly or brightly striped lengthwise, either on the top of the back (dorsum) or sides (laterally). Stripes can be white, yellow, orange, bluish, red, greenish, black, or gray. Ground colors (background) are normally yellow, gray, green, black, brown, orange, or red. Some species and subspecies have a checkered or spotted pattern in addition to the striping, but a few do not, such as the Mountain Garter, Western Black-necked Garter, and some morphs of the Northwestern Garter. Checkering or spotting is usually black. The belly is generally solidly colored with white, yellow, green, brown, gray, black, or turquoise, and may have speckling or flecks of other color present. In most species the tongue is red with a black tip. Males and females are patterned and colored similarly.

Brood Size: Live-bearing. The Black-necked Garters have 7–25 young, the Terrestrial species has 4–27 young, the Checkered Garter has 3–35 young, the Northwestern Garter has 3–20 young, and the Plains Garter has 5–90 or more young.

Range: The Terrestrial Garter Snakes are found across the western U.S., but each species has a distinct range (shown on the range maps in this chapter).

Prey: The Terrestrial Garter Snakes will prey on frogs, toads, tadpoles, worms, fish, salamanders and newts, as well as certain insects, slugs, small snakes, lizards, and small rodents, depending on what is available where they live. I once kept a Plains Garter Snake for a pet, which refused a fish I initially offered it. I then offered a large worm and the snake took it readily. Later, I offered small mice, which were also taken. The snake had been found in a dry section of the Sand Hills region of Nebraska, and there were no fish nearby, so the snake evidently didn't recognize the fish as a prey item. That scenario would not have happened with an Aquatic Garter Snake.

Habitat: Terrestrial and Aquatic. The Black-necked Garter is found from sea-level to 8,700 feet (2,700 m), the Terrestrial species from sea-level to 13,100 feet (3,990 m), the Checkered Garter from sea-level to around 7,218 feet (2,200 m), Northwestern Garter from sea-level to 5,500 feet (1,676 m), and Plains Garter from 400–7,500 feet (120–2,290 m). The Terrestrial Garter Snakes are habitat generalists, and can be found both near and far from water. Habitats include meadows, streams, wooded edge, grassland, chaparral, sand hills, pastures, seeps, open forest, and swamps.

Terrestrial Garter Snake Ranges

Left Map: Coast (Red), Mountain (Green), Wandering (Blue), Intergrade Zone (Gray).
Center Map: Plains Garter
Right Map: Western Black-necked Garter (Blue), Eastern Black-necked Garter (Red).
Bottm Right Map: Checkered Garter (Blue), NW Garter (Red).

Eastern Black-necked Garter Snake (*Thamnophis cyrtopsis ocellatus*).   Photo: Brian Hubbs

Western Black-necked Garter Snake (*Thamnophis rcyrtopsis cyrtopsis*).
Photo: Brian Hubbs

Plains Garter Snake (*Thamnophis radix*).   Photo: Brian Hubbs

Wandering Garter Snake (*Thamnophis elegans vagrans*).
Photo: Brian Hubbs

Coast Garter Snake (*Thamnophis elegans terrestris*).
Photo: Brian Hubbs

Coast Garter Snake (*Thamnophis elegans terrestris*) - Red morph.
Photo: David Jahn

Mountain Garter Snake (*Thamnophis elegans elegans*).
Photo: Brian Hubbs

Northwestern Garter Snake (*Thamnophis ordinoides*).
Photo: David Jahn

Northwestern Garter Snake (*Thamnophis ordinoides*).
Photo: David Jahn

Valley Garter Snake (*Thamnophis sirtalis fitchi*) Photo: Alan St. John

Common Garter Snake
Thamnophis sirtalis
San Francisco Garter Snake (*T. s. tetrataenia*) is Federally Protected
as an Endangered Species
California Red-sided Garter Snake (*T. s. infernalis*) is Protected in Southern CA

Subspecies: In the western U.S. there is one species of Common Garter Snake, which contains eight subspecies:

California Red-sided Garter Snake (*Thamnophis sirtalis infernalis*) Blainville, 1835 Cope, 1875 (Endangered)
Valley Garter Snake (*Thamnophis sirtalis fitchi*) Fox, 1951
Red-spotted Garter Snake (*Thamnophis sirtalis concinnus*) Hallowell, 1852
Puget Sound Garter Snake (*Thamnophis sirtalis pickeringii*) Baird & Girard, 1853
Red-sided Garter Snake (*Thamnophis sirtalis parietalis*) Say, 1823
New Mexico Garter Snake (*Thamnophis sirtalis dorsalis*) Baird & Girard, 1853
Texas Garter Snake (*Thamnophis sirtalis annectens*) Brown, 1950
Eastern Garter Snake (*Thamnophis sirtalis sirtalis*) Linnaeus, 1758
History: The Common Garter Snake was first described by Carolus Linnaeus in 1758.

Common Garter Ranges

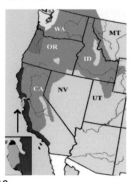

Left Map: Valley Garter (Light Blue), Red-spotted Garter (Green), Puget Sound Garter (Yellow), CA Red-sided Garter (Red), San Francisco Garter (Orange).
Right Map: Red-sided Garter (Blue), New Mexico Garter (Green), Texas Garter (Orange), Eastern Garter (Red).

Other Common Names: Garden Snake, Gardner Snake, Red-barred Garter Snake, Striped Water Snake, and Water Snake.

Size: Medium to large. Depending on the subspecies, adult Common Garter Snakes range from 18–55+ in. (46–140+ cm).

Identification: Moderately slender in build, with keeled scales and a head that is slightly wider than the neck. Most Common Garter Snakes are strongly striped lengthwise, either on the top of the back (dorsum) or sides (laterally), or both. Stripes can be white, yellow, orange, bluish, red, greenish, black, or gray. Ground colors (background) are normally yellow, gray, green, black, brown, orange, or red. A few of the subspecies have a checkered or spotted pattern in addition to the striping. Checkering or spotting is usually black. There are usually red spots, blotches, or stripes on the sides of most of these subspecies, but may not be obvious on some without close inspection. The belly is generally solidly colored with white, yellow, green, brown, gray, black, or turquoise, and may have speckling or flecks of other color present. The tongue is red with a black tip. Males and females are patterned and colored similarly. The San Francisco Garter Snake is unique in coloration and pattern, being the only subspecies with continuous red stripes (one per side) from the neck to tail. It almost always has a turquoise belly, which is faint on inland snakes east of the crest of hills, but vibrant on coastal individuals. The red stripes are each bordered by black stripes. The back (dorsal) stripe is whitish-green.

Brood Size: Live bearing, from 3–85 (average 12–20) young can be born from June to October, depending on location.

Range: The Common Garter Snake is found across the western U.S., but each subspecies has a distinct area of occupation (see range maps in this chapter).

Prey: Same as Terrestrial Garter Snake.

Habitat: Terrestrial and Aquatic. Found from sea-level to around 8,000 feet (2,438 m). The Common Garter is primarily associated with water, but will also wander great distances into dry areas in search of prey or winter shelter. They are usually found near water during the late spring and summer months, and almost anywhere in the early spring and fall.

Notes: The Common Garter Snake ranges farther north than any other snake species in North America, reaching the extreme southeastern corner of Alaska. The San Francisco Garter Snake is probably the most well-known endangered reptile in the U.S. It lost a significant portion of its population when the natural ponds along Skyline Blvd. were destroyed for housing construction in Daly City during the late 1950s and early 1960s. Since then, it has been found to occupy a significant rural portion of San Mateo County, but much of its habitat lies on private property that is managed for cattle, not snakes. An infestation of non-native Bullfrogs at many of the ponds this snake occupies continue to keep its numbers low and its populations threatened with extinction. Uncooperative land owners are part of the reason this snake remains an endangered species. Many land owners are hesitant to allow researchers to survey their land, fearing government restrictions. Their fears are baseless. They do not understand that the only way to save the snake is to identify all its populations and help them recover. I have a friend who has two populations of the snake on his land. The government has been aware of his situation for over 30 years and conducted numerous surveys at his ponds. They have never asked him to do anything, or restricted him from doing anything on his ranch. They seem to be satisfied that the snakes are persisting on the property.

The strikingly beautiful San Francisco Garter Snake (*Thamnophis sirtalis tetrataenia*).

Photo: Brian Hubbs

A juvenile California Red-sided Garter Snake (*Thamnophis sirtalis infernalis*) from Marin County.

Photo: Brian Hubbs

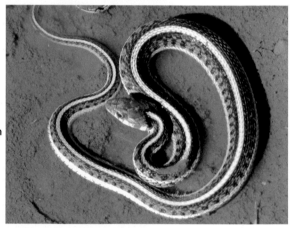

A California Red-sided Garter Snake (*Thamnophis sirtalis infernalis*) from Sonoma County. This snake was found hiding benbeath a cowpie in a pasture.

Photo: Brian Hubbs

Red-spotted Garter
Snake (*Thamnophis
sirtalis concinnus*)

Photo: David Jahn

Eastern Garter Snake (*Thamnophis s. sirtalis*) belly.
Photo: Jordan Shume

Eastern Garter Snake
(*Thamnophis s. sirtalis*)

Photo: Phil Peak

Puget Sound Garter Snake (*Thamnophis sirtalis pickeringii*).

Photo: Alan St. John

Red-sided Garter Snake (*Thamnophis sirtalis parietalis*).

Photo: Matt Cage

California Red-sided Garter Snake (*Thamnophis sirtalis infernalis*) under water in a small creek.

Photo: Brian Hubbs.

California Lyresnake (*Trimorphodon lyrophanes*) Photo: Troy Hibbitts

Lyresnakes

Trimorphodan lambda, Trimorphodan lyrophanes, & Trimorphodon vilkinsonii

Texas Lyresnake (*T. vilkinsonii*) is Protected by law in TX

Mildly Venomous

Species: Currently, there are three species of Lyresnakes recognized in the western U.S., the Sonoran Lyresnake (*Trimorphodon lambda*), California Lyresnake (*Trimorphodon lyrophanes*), and Texas Lyresnake (*Trimorphodon vilkinsonii*).

History: All three species were first described by Edward Cope, the Sonoran Lyresnake (*Trimorphodon lambda*) in 1886, the California Lyresnake (*Trimorphodon lyrophanes*) in 1860, and Texas Lyresnake (*Trimorphodon vilkinsonii*) in 1886.

Other Common Names: Jew's Harp Snake, Lyre Snake, and Wilkinson's Snake (for Texas Lyresnake).

Size: Medium to large.   Adults are 18–47¾ in. (46–121 cm).

Identification: Smooth-scaled.   Vertical, cat-like pupils.   Large head, slender neck. There is a shape on the head that resembles a lyre instrument.   Depending on the species, Lyre Snakes have a tan, light brown, or gray ground color, and darker irregular blotches with light centers down the back. The California Lyresnake has about 35 blotches, the Sonoran Lyresnake about 28, and the Texas Lyresnake about 17–24.   The belly is pale yellow to gray, often with dark speckles.

Lyresnake Range

California Lyresnake (Red)
Sonoran Lyresnake (Orange)
Texas Lyresnake (Blue)

Brood Size: Egg-layers. Clutches of 7–20 eggs have been reported.
Range: From southern California and Nevada east to southwestern Utah and the Grand Canyon, then south through the arid part of Arizona and southwestern New Mexico to the Big Bend region of Texas and adjacent Mexico.
Prey: Eats lizards, snakes, small birds, and small mammals (including bats).
Habitat: Terrestrial. Sea-level to around 7,800 feet (2,377 m). This snake is primarily found in arid mountain ranges where it occupies rocky areas, often in crevices, but also occurs in coastal chaparral. Other habitat associations include inland grassland, desert grassland, creosote bush, scrub, juniper, oak-woodland, thornscrub, thornforest, and even open coniferous forest. Occasionally it can be found in areas that have no rocks.
Notes: Injects venom into prey through enlarged grooved teeth at rear of upper jaw. Not especially dangerous to humans, but those bitten have reported mild swelling. It is probably a good idea to avoid being bitten by these serpents. The three species were once considered subspecies within the same species, but have been elevated to separate species status due to DNA examination. Stebbins (2003) only recognizes one species, with no subspecies.

Sonoran Lyresnake
(*Trimorphodon lambda*)

Photo: Brian Hubbs

Texas Lyresnake
(*Trimorphodon vilkinsonii*)

Photo: Troy Hibbitts

Lined Snake (*Tropidoclonion lineatum*)
Photo: Brian Hubbs

Lined Snake
Tropidoclonion lineatum
Protected by law in CO

Species: At one time there were four subspecies of the Lined Snake (*Tropidoclonion lineatum*), but currently none are recognized.

History: The species *Tropidoclonion lineatum* was described by Edward Hallowell in 1856.

Other Common Names: Central Lined Snake, Garden Snake, Merten's Lined Snake, Northern Lined Snake, Striped Swamp Snake, and Texas Lined Snake.

Size: Small. These snakes range from 4–22½ in. (10–57 cm) in total length.

Identification: Keeled-scales. Grayish to olive above, with a light stripe of yellow, white, gray, orange, or reddish the length of the back and tail. There is also a lighter, less defined stripe along each lower side. The stripes are usually bordered by small dark spots. The belly is light colored with two rows of dark, crescent shaped spots down the center (which may or may not be fused together.

Brood Size: Live-bearing. Number of young can range from 2-17.

Range: Found from eastern New Mexico and eastern Colorado to southeastern South Dakota and portions of Iowa, then south to southeastern Texas. There are two disjunct areas of occupation in Illinois, and one disjunct area in south Texas.

Prey: Favorite food is earthworms.

Habitat: Terrestrial. Found from sea-level to near 6,562 feet (2,000 m) in prairie, high desert grassland, woods, vacant lots, dumps, and along streams, often under flat rocks and other surface debris during the

Lined Snake Range

emergence season. In the western portion of their range in New Mexico these snakes are extremely common in moist areas, such as along intermittent streams and seeps, but might turn up almost anywhere.

Notes: Related to the Garter Snakes. Abundant, but spotty in distribution over much of the western part of its range.

Lined Snake (*Tropidoclonion lineatum*)   Photo: Matt Cage

Western Smooth Earth Snake (*Virginia valeriae elegans*).
Photo: Troy Hibbitts

Earth Snakes
Virginia valeriae & Virginia striatula
Both Protected by law in KS

Species & Subspecies: The Western Smooth Earth Snake (*Virginia valeriae elegans*) and Rough Earth Snake (*Virginia striatula*) occur within the area of this book. Two other Smooth Earth Snake subspecies are found in the eastern U.S.

History: The Smooth Earth Snake (*Virginia valeriae*) was described by Baird and Girard in 1853, and the subspecies *Virginia valeriae elegans* was described by Robert Kennicott in 1859. The Rough Earth Snake (*Virginia striatula*) was described by Carolus Linnaeus in 1766.

Other Common Names: Blaney's Snake, Brown Snake, Eastern Gray Snake, Eastern Ground Snake, Garden Snakes, Gray Snakes, Ground Snakes, Kennicott's Brown Snake, Little Brown Snakes, Spotted Ground Snake, Valeria Blaney's Snake, Valeria's Snake, Virginia Snake, Virginia's snake, and Worm Snake.

Size: Small. Adult Smooth and Rough Earth Snakes average 7–10 in. (18–25.4 cm) with a record size of 15⅜ in. (39.3 cm) for the Smooth species and 12¾ in.(32.4 cm) for the Rough species.

Identification: Smooth Earth Snakes have smooth scales and are reddish brown or gray with a possible faint lighter stripe down the back and small dark spots that may

Smooth Earth Snake
Range

Rough Earth Snake
Range

loosely form two to four rows down the back. The belly is plain whitish or yellowish. Rough Earth Snakes are similarly colored but without the light stripe or much spotting, and have keeled (ridged) scales. Both have pointed snouts.

Brood Size: Live-bearing. The Rough Earth Snake gives birth to 3–8 young, while the Smooth Earth Snake usually has 4–12 young.

Range: Smooth Earth Snakes are found from eastern Texas and Oklahoma to southern Iowa, and eastward to the Atlantic states. Rough Earth Snakes are found from central Texas and eastern Oklahoma to the southern half of Missouri and eastward to the Piedmont and Coastal Plain in Virginia, North Carolina, South Carolina, Georgia, and extreme northern Florida.

Prey: Primarily earthworms and other soft-bodied insects.

Habitat: Terrestrial. Areas with moist, loose soil for burrowing, including deciduous forest, old fields, and forest edge.

Notes: One of the "Garden" snakes that might be found in a well-tilled backyard in rural areas. This snake can be locally abundant or scarce depending on the habitat. They are probably extremely common, but due to their subterranean nature are not often seen.

Rough Earth Snake (*Virginia striatula*).   Photo: Troy Hibbitts

References

Books

Boundy, Jeff. 2006. *Snakes of Louisiana*. Louisiana Department of Wildlife and Fisheries. Baton Rouge, Louisiana.

Conant, Roger and Joseph T. Collins. 1998. *Reptiles and Amphibians, Eastern/Central North America*. Houghton Mifflin Co. Boston/New York.

Degenhardt, William, et al. 1996. *Amphibians and Reptiles of New Mexico*. University of New Mexico Press. Albuquerque, New Mexico.

Collins, Joseph T. and Travis Taggart. 2010. *Amphibians, Reptiles, and Turtles in Kansas*. Eagle Mountain Publishing, LC. Eagle Mountain, Utah.

Fogell, Daniel. 2010. *A Field Guide to the Amphibians and Reptiles of Nebraska*. University of Nebraska, Lincoln.

Holycross, Andrew T. and Tom C. Brennan. 2006. *Amphibians and Reptiles in Arizona*. Arizona Game and Fish Department. Phoenix, Arizona.

Hubbs, Brian. 2004. *Mountain Kings*. Tricolor Books. Tempe, Arizona.

Hubbs, Brian. 2009. *Common Kingsnakes*. Tricolor Books. Tempe, Arizona.

Johnson, Tom R. 1997. *The Amphibians and Reptiles of Missouri*. Missouri Dept. of Conservation. Jefferson City, Missouri.

Kiesow, Alyssa M. 2006. *Field Guide to Amphibians and Reptiles of South Dakota*. South Dakota Dept. of Game, Fish and Parks. Pierre, South Dakota.

St. John, Alan. 2002. *Reptiles of the Northwest*. Lone Pine Publishing. Renton, Washington.

Stebbins, Robert C. 2003. *Western Reptiles and Amphibians*. Third edition, Houghton Mifflin Co., Boston.

—. 1985. *A Field Guide to Western Reptiles and Amphibians*. Houghton Mifflin Co., Boston.

—. 1954. *Amphibians and Reptiles of Western North America*. McGraw-Hill, Inc., New York.

Tennant, Alan. 1984. *The Snakes of Texas*. Texas Monthly Press, Austin, Texas.

Werner, J. Kirwin, et al. 2004. *Amphibians and Reptiles of Montana*. Mountain Press Publishing, Missoula, Montana.

Wright, A. H. and A. A. Wright. 1957. *Handbook of Snakes*. Vol. 1 & Vol. 2, Comstock Publishing Associates, Ithaca, New York.

Websites

Arkansas Herp Atlas: www.herpsofarkansas.com

Beltz, Ellen. *Biographys of People Honored*: http://ebeltz.net

Kansas Herp Atlas: http://webcat.fhsu.edu/ksfauna/herps/

Missouri Herp Atlas: http://atlas.moherp.org/

Nafis, Gary. *California Herps*: www.californiaherps.com/index.html

Southwestern Center of Herpetological Research: www.southwesternherp.com

SSAR. *Scientific and Standard English Names of Amphibians and Reptiles of North America North of Mexico, With Comments Regarding Confidence In Our Understanding*. Edition 6.1. www.ssarherps.org/pages/comm_names/Index.php

Notes